BEST LOVED
SONGS AND HYMNS

BEST LOVED SONGS AND HYMNS

Popular, Patriotic and Folk Songs
Church Hymns and Gospel Songs
Spirituals and Carols

Edited by
JAMES MOREHEAD
and
ALBERT MOREHEAD

Funk & Wagnalls
New York

Published in Canada by Fitzhenry & Whiteside Limited, Toronto.

Library of Congress Catalog Card Number 75-13671

ISBN 0-308-10178-2

FOREWORD

THESE ARE THE SONGS that most of us have known all our lives. Our mothers crooned them as they bent over our cradles, our fathers sang them robustly about the house, we sang them with our schoolmates and our first sweethearts. Among them are songs that have restored faith, inspired armies, swayed public opinion, and told the course of empire; but most of the songs have been selected because so many people, for such a long time, have found them good to sing. For that reason they will be as familiar as old friends.

All arrangements are in four-part harmony, playable on piano, organ, or accordion. Except for the hymns and sacred songs, there are diagrams for ukulele and symbols for guitar. The ukulele chords have been simplified so that a novice can master the fingering with ease. The vocal arrangements, with few exceptions, have been made adaptable to various combinations of voices, even when a full quartet is not available, and also practical for unison singing, since the melody remains in the "top note" throughout.

SOURCES OF SONGS. To trace composers, authors and translators of many songs; to untangle the maze of error, perpetuated over many years as each "new" songbook copied from its predecessors, editors must become detectives. Sometimes their best efforts end in failure and in sincere regret—for example, that the translator of *La Paloma* should himself remain unsung while his work is sung and loved throughout the English-speaking world.

In some cases, omissions from the "catalog of the public domain" are all but incredible. The editors have tried to repair these omissions.

For example, after literally months of searching the editors could find no translation of *La Marseillaise*; the "prevailing English version" is hardly even a paraphrase. In several other cases, translations were found to exist but to lack the indispensable quality of a song lyric— they are not singable. We have supplied translations for these songs.

HYMNS. Our selection embraces some classical hymns and hymns sung frequently in formal church services, but chiefly we present those more informal numbers called "Sunday School hymns," "Gospel hymns," or "sacred songs." This book is not a hymnal and its purpose —to provide words and music for singing at home and in informal groups—can better be served by songs having moderate range and high melodic quality.

In making our selections we have had the advice of clergymen and laymen of all denominations, in all sections of the United States, and in Canada. *Christian Herald* magazine very generously conducted a poll of its hundreds of thousands of readers on our behalf, and we relied heavily on the preferences they expressed; we thank the magazine's editor, Dr. Daniel A. Poling, and Dr. Clarence W. Hall, then its executive editor, now senior editor of *The Reader's Digest*, for this assistance. Several pastors polled their congregations on our behalf and to them too we give our thanks.

All our selections have been made on merit; we have not had to make a single omission on account of copyright restrictions. The copyright owners kindly granted us permission for every one that we wanted to include, and we take this opportunity to express our gratitude to them.

So that we might display both words and music as large as possible, we omitted the terminal Amen from the hymns but supplied a musical arrangement for every key; these appear on the last page of this book. The pianist, organist or choral director can turn to this page almost without pause to find the music appropriate to his selection.

BALLADS. Here we cannot say, as we did in the case of our hymnodic selections, that copyright restrictions were no problem. Publishers of popular music in the United States—the group generally called "Tin Pan Alley"—as a matter of policy and mutual agreement do not release their copyrights for republication in anthologies such as this.

Nevertheless the editors found this policy cause for regret in only two or perhaps three cases. The statutory copyright in the United States expires after fifty-six years. Usually it takes longer than that for a song to become a true "standard" and much, much longer for it to merit classification as a "folk song."

Longevity is a primary requirement for a "best-loved" song. Songs may become popular very quickly, but they can lose their popularity almost as quickly. The editors have been acutely conscious of trends. Forty years ago it would have been unthinkable to leave "The Old Oaken Bucket" out of such a book as this; today that song does not qualify. With the exception of some patriotic or inspirational songs, the most recent applicants that are best-known and -loved today date from the 1890's and early 1900's. Incidentally, we use the designation "Gay 'Nineties" for some songs that were actually written shortly after the turn of the century, because they are in the same spirit.

FOLK SONGS. There are few really great songs. The most famous melodies are basic and of great antiquity. Many of our folk songs derive from tunes that were known to the bards and troubadours; they have endured, with slight changes, for hundreds or thousands of years.

The editors of this compilation have elected in most cases to present these songs as they are actually sung. No attempt has been made to formalize such songs as *John Henry, The Old Chisholm Trail, Barb'ry Allen;* we transcribe them as we have heard them. Some songs, or versions of songs, here appear in print for the first time. For example the spiritual *Lord I'm Troublin'*, here presented as sung by a group of field hands on a South Carolina plantation. All efforts to uncover a printed version have failed, yet W. C. Handy, in his eightieth year, informed us that he remembered it from the time he was five years old.

We have not hesitated, where we think it appropriate, to present the words as they have been adapted by successive generations, rather than the historic versions that scholarly anthologies may pardonably consider obligatory. An example might be "Yankee Doodle" or some lyrics of Stephen C. Foster. Such deviations (which we will note in our prefatory comments) should be considered a matter of editorial judgment and not inadequate research.

ACKNOWLEDGMENTS. First, to J. Franklin Whitman, who designed this book and executed the beautifully decorative end pages. Louis Pennino engraved the music, and Jane Derrick McDowell and Earle Pitts prepared the copy for the printers. The late William C. Handy in folk music and Dr. Reginald McAll in hymnology were valuable personal consultants, and of course, like all who delve into American music, the editors are indebted to the works of John and Alan Lomax, Sigmund Spaeth, David Ewen, and others.

JAMES MOREHEAD
ALBERT MOREHEAD

New York 1965

CONTENTS

CONTENTS viii

PATRIOTIC SONGS

AMERICA

Samuel Francis Smith

Uncertain origin

Mr. Smith, a Boston minister, wrote the American words for a service at the Park Street Church on July 4, 1831, taking the melody from a German songbook lent him by Lowell Mason and unaware that it was the tune of the British national anthem (see facing page). Until *The Star-Spangled Banner* was made official in 1931 this was a prime candidate for the national anthem of the United States and most Americans still stand up for it. Henry Carey was once credited with the tune, based on a claim made by his son after his death, but this claim has been discredited, though without stigma on Carey. Other British and continental claims have proved equally unreliable and none seems now to have hope of verification. Union of words and music in *God Save the King* has not been traced back beyond 1743, though both are very likely older.

1. My coun - try, 'tis of thee,
2. My na - tive coun - try, thee,
3. Let mu - sic swell the breeze,
4. Our fa - thers' God, to Thee,

Sweet land of lib - er - ty, Of thee I
Land of the no - ble free, Thy name I
And ring from all the trees Sweet free - dom's
Au - thor of lib - er - ty, To Thee we

sing. Land where my fa - thers died!
love. I love thy rocks and rills,
song. Let mor - tal tongues a - wake;
sing. Long may our land be bright

Land	of	the	Pil - grims' pride! From ev' - ry ___
Thy	woods	and	tem - pled hills; My heart ___ with ___
Let	all	that	breathe par - take; Let rocks ___ their ___
With	free - dom's	ho -	ly light; Pro - tect ___ us ___

moun - tain	side,	Let ___ free - dom	ring!
rap - ture	thrills	Like ___ that a -	bove.
si - lence	break,	The ___ sound pro -	long.
by	Thy might,	Great ___ God, our	King!

God Save the Queen

THE TITLE FLUCTUATES according to the sex of the British monarch, but most often it is GOD SAVE THE KING. By authoritative proclamation in 1931, only the tune is the British national anthem, the words being unofficial. Most stanzas date from the early 18th century and are recited below in the form best reputed since the accession of Elizabeth II.

1. God save our gracious Queen,
Long live our noble Queen,
 God save the Queen!
Send her victorious,
Happy and glorious,
Long to reign over us,
 God save the Queen!

2. O Lord, our God, arise,
Scatter our enemies
 And make them fall;
Confound their politics,
Frustrate their knavish tricks.
On Him our hopes we fix.
 O save us all!

3. Of many a race and birth,
From utmost ends of earth,
 God save us all.
Did strife and hatred cease,
Did hope and joy increase,
Spread universal peace.
 God save us all.

4. Nor on this land alone,
But be God's mercies shown
 From shore to shore.
Lord, make the nations see
That men should brothers be
And form one family
 The wide world o'er.

THE STAR-SPANGLED BANNER

FRANCIS SCOTT KEY

JOHN STAFFORD SMITH

THE TUNE of THE STAR-SPANGLED BANNER was popular in America before the words were written; it was originally called *To Anacreon in Heaven*, and was written for the Anacreontic Society of London, about 1775. Key wrote the inspired text as a prisoner on a British ship that was bombarding Fort McHenry (at Baltimore) in 1814. Just before dawn the firing stopped, and with daybreak those on the ship could see the flag still flying over the fort.

With Spirit

1. Oh— say! can you see, by the dawn's ear - ly
2. On the shore, dim - ly seen thro' the mists of the
3. Oh,— thus be it ev - er when free men shall

light, What so proud - ly we hailed at the twi-light's last
deep, Where the foe's haugh - ty host in dread si - lence re -
stand Be - tween their lov'd homes and the war's de - so -

gleam - ing? Whose broad stripes and bright stars thro' the
pos - es, What is that which the breeze, o'er the
la - tion! Blest with vic - t'ry and peace, may the

per - il - ous fight, O'er the ram-parts we watch'd, were so
tow - er - ing steep, As it fit - ful - ly blows, half con -
heav'n-res - cued land Praise the Pow'r that hath made and pre -

4

5

AMERICA THE BEAUTIFUL

KATHERINE LEE BATES   SAMUEL A. WARD

ONE OF THE great patriotic songs of the United States, this was written in 1893 by Miss Bates, who was Professor of English at Wellesley
College, to the hymn tune *Materna*. Shortly before writing it she
had made a trip to the West, and from the summit of Pike's Peak
had seen "spacious skies" above the "fruited plains."

1. O beau-ti-ful for spa-cious skies, For
2. O beau-ti-ful for pil-grim feet Whose
3. O beau-ti-ful for he-roes prov'd In
4. O beau-ti-ful for pa-triot dream That

am-ber waves of grain,__ For pur-ple moun-tain
stern im-pas-sion'd stress__ A thor-ough-fare for
lib-er-at-ing strife,__ Who more than self their
sees be-yond the years,__ Thine al-a-bas-ter

maj-es-ties A-bove the fruit-ed plain.__ A-
free-dom beat A-cross the wil-der-ness.__ A-
coun-try lov'd And mer-cy more than life.__ A-
cit-ies gleam, Un-dimmed by hu-man tears.__ A-

THE BATTLE HYMN OF THE REPUBLIC

Julia Ward Howe

Ascribed to William Steffe

WHILE MRS. HOWE was visiting in Washington during the Civil War, she heard the Union soldiers singing "John Brown's Body" to the tune of a popular Sunday-school hymn. The melody remained in her mind, and during the night she wrote her magnificent lyric. The result was this classic marching song, known and sung all over the world, even where it has no patriotic significance. Its thunderous eloquence is not exceeded anywhere in the realm of patriotic poetry, and may be equalled only by the *Marseillaise*.

1. Mine eyes have seen the glo - ry of the
2. I have seen Him in the watch-fires of a
3. He has sound - ed forth the trum - pet that shall
4. In the beau - ty of the lil - ies Christ was

com - ing of the Lord; He is
hun - dred cir - cling camps; They have
nev - er call re - treat; He is
born a - cross the sea; With a

tramp - ling out the vin - tage where the
build - ed Him an al - tar in the
sift - ing out the hearts of men be -
glo - ry in His bos - om that trans -

grapes of wrath are stored; He hath
eve - ning dews and damps; I can
fore His judg - ment seat; Oh, be
fig - ures you and me; As He

loosed the fate - ful light - ning of His
read His right - eous sen - tence by the
swift, my soul, to an - swer Him! be
died to make men ho - ly, let us

ter - ri - ble swift sword. His truth is march-ing on.
dim and flar - ing lamps. His day is march-ing on.
ju - bi - lant, my feet! Our God is march-ing on.
die to make men free, While God is march-ing on.

Glo - ry! glo - ry hal - le - lu - jah!

Glo - ry! glo - ry hal - le - lu - jah! Glo - ry! glo - ry hal - le -

lu - jah! His truth is march - ing on.

THE ARMY GOES ROLLING ALONG

Edmund L. Gruber; H. W. Arberg

Edmund L. Gruber

FOR NEARLY HALF A CENTURY every American knew "The caissons go rolling along," written by General Gruber (when he was a lieutenant) for his beloved Field Artillery and expanded by John Philip Sousa to the formal *Field Artillery March.* When artillery faded under airpower, and coincidentally the U. S. Army wished to adopt an official song, Dr. Arberg was in charge of selection. He adapted Gruber's 1909 original and Sousa's 1918 expansion, and this is the result—still a classic.

1. First to fight for the right, and to build the Nation's might, and The Ar - my goes roll - ing a - long.____ Proud of all we have done, Fight - ing till the bat - tle's

2. Val - ley Forge, Cus - ter's ranks, San Juan Hill and Pat - ton's tanks, and The Ar - my went roll - ing a - long.____ Min - ute men from the start, Al - ways fight - ing from the

3. Men in rags, men who froze, still that Ar - my met its foes, and The Ar - my went roll - ing a - long.____ Faith in God, then we're right, And we'll fight with all our

ANCHORS AWEIGH

ALFRED H. MILES

CHARLES A. ZIMMERMAN

ZIMMERMAN, BANDMASTER at the U. S. Naval Academy (Annapolis), collaborated with Miles when the former was a lieutenant and the latter a midshipman. The song was first sung at the Army-Navy football game of 1906 (and Navy won). The public treats ANCHOR'S AWEIGH (the apostrophe is proper) as the theme song of the United States Navy; enlisted men in the Navy have never quite shared that view, considering it the officers' song, although they too take pride in it.

1. Stand Navy down the field, Sails set to the sky,_____ We'll never change our course, So Army you steer
2. Get under way, Navy, Decks cleared for the fray,_____ We'll hoist true Navy Blue, So Army down your
3. Blue of the seven seas, Gold of God's great sun,_____ Let these our colors be Till all of time be

13

THE NAVY HYMN

WILLIAM WHITING   **JOHN BACCHUS DYKES**

THIS IS the most widely used hymn addressed to the Father of sea-
farers Who created the waters, Whose power can soothe the storm
(MATTHEW 8:23). It is always a part of the service on British ships,
and is the official hymn of the United States Naval Academy.

1. E - ter - nal Fa - ther! strong to save, Whose
2. O Sav - iour, whose al - might - y word The
3. O sa - cred Spir - it, who didst brood Up -
4. O Trin - i - ty of love and pow'r! Our

arm doth bind the rest - less wave, Who
winds and waves sub - mis - sive heard, Who
on the cha - os dark and rude, Who
breth - ren shield in dan - ger's hour; From

bid'st the might - y o - cean deep Its
walk - edst in the foam - ing deep, And
bad'st its an - gry tu - mult cease, And
rock and tem - pest, fire and foe, Pro -

14

own ap - point-ed lim - its keep; O
calm a - mid its rage didst sleep; O
gav - est light, and life, and peace; O
tect them where-so - e'er they go, Thus

hear us when we cry to Thee, For
hear us when we cry to Thee For
hear us when we cry to Thee For
ev - er let there rise to Thee Glad

those in per - il on the sea.
those in per - il on the sea!
those in per - il on the sea!
hymns of praise from land and sea!

THE MARINES' HYMN

ANONYMOUS

THE MARINES' HYMN is historically older than most other American patriotic songs, as is attested by the first two lines referring to the war against the Barbary Pirates of North Africa and the Mexican War (whence the reference to the Halls of Montezuma). All attempts to trace the origin have met with failure.

1. From the Halls of Mon-te-zu - ma To the
2. Here's health to you and to our Corps Which

shores of Trip-o-li___ We fight our
we are proud to serve;— In man-y a

coun-try's bat - tles On the land as on the sea.
strife we've fought for life And nev-er lost our nerve.

First to fight for right and free -
If the Ar - my and the Na -

dom And to keep our hon - or clean, ___
vy Ev - er look on Heav - en's scenes, ___

We are proud to claim the ti -
They will find the streets are guard-

tle Of U - nit - ed States Ma - rines. ___
ed By U - nit - ed States Ma - rines! ___

THE AIR FORCE BLUE

SCOTT-TEXTOR

THERE IS SOME CONTROVERSY as to whether the United States Air Force has ever had an official song—the Air Force has taken no such action since it succeeded the U. S. Army Air Corps in 1947—but this is the song bought from its writers by the Air Force, for use as a recuiting song, and placed in the public domain so that it can be freely reprinted. The "blue" in the title has a double meaning, representing both the uniform and the sky.

They took the 1. blue from the skies, And a
2. men with a dream On A-

pret - ty girl's eyes, And a touch of Old
mer - i - ca's team, They're a rug - ged and

Glo - ry's hue, _____ And gave it to the
read - y crew, _____ And you can bet your

men, Who proud - ly wear The The U. S.
boots, The world looks up To

1.   2.   3. *Fine*

Air Force Blue!___ Oh they are ___ They ___

know where they're go - ing, They've set their course; The

D. S. 𝄋 al Fine

sky's no lim - it in the Air Force! They took the

YANKEE DOODLE

AUTHOR UNKNOWN

YANKEE DOODLE is the subtitle of the famous painting "The Spirit of '76." Sigmund Spaeth, after citing several pages of sober (and conflicting) views by historians, says: "It is a safe guess that YANKEE DOODLE was originally an instrumental tune, coming to this country from England, Scotland, or Ireland, with various texts added from time to time."

Yan-kee Doo-dle went to town
Yan-kee Doo-dle went to town, To
Fath'r and I went down to camp, A-
And there we saw a thou-sand men, As
And there was Cap-tain Wash-ing-ton Up-

Rid-ing on a po-ny,
buy a pair of trou-sers, He
long with Cap-tain Good-win, And
rich as Squire Da-vid, And
on a slap-ping stal-lion, A-

Stuck a feath-er in his crown, And
swore he could not see the town Be-
there we saw the men and boys As
what they wast-ed ev-'ry day, I
giv-ing or-ders to his men; I

called it mac - a - ro - ni.
cause of all the hous - es.
thick as hast - y pud - din'.
wish it could be sav - ed.
guess there was a mil - lion.

CHORUS

Yan - kee Doo - dle, keep it up,

Yan - kee Doo - dle dan - dy; Mind the mu - sic

and the step, And with the girls be han - dy.

DIXIE

Daniel Decatur Emmett

A MEASURE of the quality of DIXIE is that Abraham Lincoln loved to hear it, and Northern soldiers sang it, even though it represented the enemy. It was written as a "walk-around" for Dan Bryant's Minstrel Show in New York. There are many conflicting stories as to how it came to mean the land below the Mason-Dixon line (probably a pure accident); but there is no doubt that it was the great inspirational song of the Confederacy.

O CANADA!

R. STANLEY WEIR (English)
ADOLPHE ROUTHIER (French)

CALIXA LAVALLÉE

THIS GREAT SONG, the product in music of one of Canada's great composers, and in its words of two of Canada's eminent jurists, was completed in its various forms at the turn of the century. Mr. Weir called it "a humble effort to do a great thing: to supply Canada with a National Song." The result, far from humble, was worthy of its purpose; but the reception ran afoul of politics. French-Canadian in inception, the anthem failed to displace the popular *The Maple Leaf Forever*; in 1965 the argument is unabated.

1. O Can - a - da! Our home and na - tive land!__ True pa - triot - love in all thy sons com - mand. With glow - ing hearts we__ see thee rise The__
2. O Can - a - da! Where pines and ma - ples grow, __ Great prai - ries spread and lord - ly riv - ers flow, How__ dear to us thy__ broad do - main, From__
3. O Can - a - da! Be - neath thy shin - ing skies __ May stal - wart sons and gen - tle maid - ens rise; To__ keep thee stead - fast__ through the years From__
4. Rul - er su - preme, who hear - est hum - ble prayer, __ Hold our Do - min - ion in Thy lov - ing care. Help__ us to find, O__ God, in Thee A __

THE MAPLE LEAF FOREVER

Alexander Muir

Alexander Muir was born in Scotland, but was brought to Canada at the age of three. After graduating from Queen's University he became a song writer. The Maple Leaf Forever is regarded as the national song of Canada. The words refer to the hero of Canadian history, James Wolfe, who defeated Montcalm at Quebec and so gave "New France" to the English crown. Nootka Sound is on Vancouver Island, all the way across the continent.

1. In days of yore, from Brit-ain's shore, Wolfe the daunt-less he-ro came, And plant-ed firm Bri-tan-nia's flag, On Can-a-da's fair do-main; Here may it wave, our boast and pride, And

2. Our fair Do-min-ion now ex-tends From Cape Race to Noot-ka Sound, May peace for-ev-er be our lot, And plen-te-ous store a-bound; And may those ties of love be ours, Which

join in love to-geth-er, The This-tle, Sham-rock,
dis-cord can-not sev-er, And flour-ish green o'er

Rose en-twine The Ma-ple Leaf for-ev-er.
Free-dom's home, The Ma-ple Leaf for-ev-er.

CHORUS
The Ma-ple Leaf, our em-blem dear, The

Ma-ple Leaf for-ev-er, God save our King and

Heav-en bless The Ma-ple Leaf for-ev-er.

RULE BRITANNIA

JAMES THOMSON

THOMAS AUGUSTINE ARNE

RULE BRITANNIA, the national song of Great Britain, was originally an ode sung in the masque *Alfred*, the music for which was composed by Arne in 1739. The masque was later made into an opera (1745) but the ode was retained. Handel used the melody in his *Occasional Oratorios*.

1. When Brit-ain first,— at Heav'n's com-mand, A-
2. The mus-es, still— with free-dom found, Shall

rose— from out the az-ure main, A-
to— thy hap-py coast— re-pair, Shall

rose from out— the az-ure main,
to thy hap- py coast re-pair;

This was the char-ter, the char-ter of the land, And
Blest Isle of free-dom, with match-less beau-ty crown'd, And

guard-ian an - gels sang this strain:
man - ly hearts to guard the fair,

Rule, Bri-tan-nia, Bri-tan-nia rule the waves,

never, never, nev-er
Bri-tons nev - er shall be slaves. shall be slaves.

LA MARSEILLAISE

Tr. ALBERT MOREHEAD   CLAUDE JOSEPH ROUGET DE LISLE

ROUGET DE LISLE, a young French officer, wrote the words and almost as surely the music at Strasbourg in 1792; the song received its name when revolutionaries from Marseilles sang it so enthusiastically later that year. Beethoven and many other composers have used the musical theme. The first stanza, unsurpassed in patriotic poetry, in English versions is usually only paraphrased; here it is translated except for the closing lines, which mean "Let [their] impure blood irrigate our fields!"

Come sons of France, march on to
Al - lons, en - fants de la Pa -

vic - to - ry! The day of glo - ry is at hand. For the
tri - e, Le jour de gloire est ar - ri - vé, Con - tre

ty - rant march-es a-gainst us, On his flag the blood of our
nous, de la ty - ran - ni e L'é - ten - dard san-glant est le -

land; On his flag is the blood of our land. And do you
vé, L'é - ten - dard san-glant est le - vé. En - ten - dez-

hear these vile ma-raud — ers who roar like beasts in our
vous, dan ces cam-pa-gnes, Mu-gir ces fé ro ces sol-

farms? Who tear our loved ones from our arms,— Who at-
dats? Ils vien-nent jus-que dans nos bras,— E-gor-

tack our wives, our sons and daugh-ters? To arms,— men of
ger nos fils, nos com-pa-gnes! Aux ar — mes, Ci-toy-

France! Close ranks— As we ad-vance! March on, march on;
ens, For-mez — vos ba-tail-lons! Mar-chons, mar-chons,

Long live our land, And death— to foes of France!—
Qu'un sang im-pur A-breu — ve nos sil-lons!—

31

THE WEARING OF THE GREEN

Revised by DION BOUCICAULT

DURING the Irish Rebellion of 1796, members of the Volunteers were identified by their insignia, the green shamrock. When they were caught, the penalty was execution. Their leader and hero was James Napper Tandy, an Irish patriot who attempted an independence movement modeled on the American Revolution. The tune is also that of the old West Point song *Benny Havens, Oh!*

1. O__ Pad - dy, dear, and did you hear the news that's go - ing 'round? The sham - rock is for - bid by law to grow on I - rish ground; I__ met with Nap - per Tan - dy and he

2. Saint__ Pat - rick's day no more we'll keep, his col - or can't be seen, For there's a blood - y law a - gin' the wear - in' o' the green.

tuk me by the hand, And he said, "How's poor ould
Ire - land, and how___ does she stand?"
She's the most dis - tress - ful coun - try___ that
ev - er you have seen; They're hang - ing men and
wo - men there for wear - ing of the green.

THE PLEDGE TO THE FLAG

Francis Bellamy   James Morehead

THE WORDS OF THE PLEDGE are official by Act of Congress; a brief but well-researched history of them may be read in *World Almanac.* The beautifully rhythmic text of Bellamy's original has been wounded twice: by including *of the United States of America*, lest unreconstructed rebels might secretly mean the Confederate flag; and by the insertion in 1954 of the words *under God*, by legislators who presumably believed that there can be a nation that is not under God.

I pledge al - le-giance to the flag —— of the U - nit - ed States of A - mer - i - ca And to the Re - pub - lic for which it stands, One na - tion, un - der God, in - di - vis - i - ble, With lib - er - ty and jus - tice for all. ——

34

SENTIMENTAL BALLADS

BEAUTIFUL DREAMER

Stephen C. Foster

Stephen Foster's "last song, written only a few days before his death." It was published in 1864, shortly after he died (at the age of 38). His work had deteriorated greatly during the last few years of his life, and it is not unreasonable to suppose that this song, one of his finest efforts, was an earlier composition, unearthed and perhaps revised to make an immediate sale.

Beau - ti - ful dream - er, wake un - to me,

Star - light and dew-drops are wait - ing for thee,—

Sounds of the rude world, heard in the day,

Lull'd by the moon - light have all passed a - way.—

DRINK TO ME ONLY WITH THINE EYE

BEN JONSON

Old English Tune

BEN JONSON'S *Song, To Celia* was published in a volume of poems in 1616. It is certainly as well known, and well loved, as any song in the English language. The origin of the tune remains a mystery; it is probably from the 16th century.

1. Drink to me on-ly with thine eyes, And
2. I sent thee late a ros-y wreath, Not

I will pledge with mine;___
so much hon-'ring thee___

Or leave a kiss but in the cup And
As giv-ing it a hope that there It

I'll   not look for   wine.   The
could   not with-ered   be;   But

thirst that from the   soul doth rise   Doth
thou there - on didst   on - ly breathe   And

ask a drink di - vine; But might I   of Jove's
sent'st it back to   me; Since when it grows, and

nec - tar sup I would not change for thine.
smells, I swear, Not of   it - self but thee!

HOW CAN I LEAVE THEE?

FRIEDRICH WILHELM KÜCKEN

THERE IS no doubt that Kücken himself wrote the beautiful German song *Ach, wie ist's möglich dann,* about 1827, but several early editions failed to credit him, including a Baltimore publication of 1851. In English translation his melody has been popular for more than one hundred years. It is sometimes known as *Thuringian Folk Song,* and often listed as anonymous. Kücken, the son of a peasant, distinguished himself in music and became tutor to German princes.

1. How can I leave thee! How can I from thee part! Thou on-ly hast my heart, Dear one, be-lieve.
2. Blue is a flow'r-et Called the "For-get-me-not," Wear it up-on thy heart, And think of me!
3. Would I a bird were! Soon at thy side to be, Fal-con nor hawk would fear, Speed-ing to thee.

Thou hast this soul of mine
Flow'r - et and hope may die,
When by the fowl - er slain,

So close - ly bound to thine, No oth - er
Yet love with us shall stay, That can-not
I at thy feet should lie, Thou sad-ly

can I love, Save thee a - lone!
pass a - way, Dear one, be - lieve.
shouldst com - plain, Joy - ful I'd die.

CARELESS LOVE

ANONYMOUS

No OTHER folk song is better known than CARELESS LOVE, and there is no doubt about the universality of its theme, with the closing resolution: "Going to cry tonight...and cry no more."

1 Love, oh, love, oh, care - less love, Love, oh, love, oh, care - less love, Oh, well it's
2 Sor - row, sor - row to my heart, Sor - row, sor - row to my heart, Oh, well it's
3 (I) cried last night and the night be - fore, (I) cried last night and the night be - fore, Oh, well I

FLOW GENTLY, SWEET AFTON

ROBERT BURNS

JAMES E. SPILMAN

THIS SCOTTISH SONG was set to music, at least in America, by a Philadelphian, James E. Spilman, in 1838. In Scotland and the British Commonwealth it usually is titled *Afton Water*, with a tune by Alexander Hume. The interval of a sixth, in the sixth and twelfth measures, is common to both melodies. Spilman's tune is used for *Away In A Manger* also.

1. Flow gen-tly, sweet Af-ton, a-mang thy green braes; Flow gen-tly, I'll sing thee a song in thy praise; My Ma-ry's a-sleep by thy mur-mur-ing stream, Flow gen-tly, sweet Af-ton, dis-turb not her

2. How loft-y, sweet Af-ton, thy neigh-bor-ing hills, Far marked with the cours-es of clear-wind-ing rills! There dai-ly I wan-der, as morn ris-es high, My flocks and my Ma-ry's sweet cot in my

3. Thy crys-tal stream, Af-ton, how love-ly it glides, And winds by the cot where my Ma-ry re-sides! How wan-ton thy wa-ters her snow-y feet lave, As, gath-'ring sweet flow-'rets, she stems thy clear

dream. Thou stock-dove, whose ech - o re - sounds from the
eye. How pleas - ant thy banks and green val - leys be -
wave! Flow gen - tly, sweet Af - ton, a - mang thy green

hill, Ye wild whist - ling black - birds in
low, Where wild in the wood - lands the
braes, Flow gen - tly, sweet riv - er, the

yon thorn - y dell, Thou green - crest - ed
prim - ros - es blow! There oft, as mild
theme of my lays; My Ma - ry's a

lap - wing, thy scream - ing for - bear, I
eve - ning creeps o - ver the lea, The
sleep by thy mur - mur - ing stream, Flow

charge you, dis - turb not my slum - ber - ing fair.
sweet - scent - ed birk shades my Ma - ry and me.
gen - tly, sweet Af - ton, dis - turb not her dream.

45

IN THE GLOAMING

META ORRED   **ANNIE F. HARRISON**

A NEW WORD was added to the lexicon of popular songs when Meta Orred and Annie F. Harrison wrote IN THE GLOAMING and introduced it in England in 1877. The song has been given the consideration of an art song, appearing on many concert programs. Sigmund Spaeth says that it "definitely belongs among the better products of popular music."

1. In the gloam-ing oh,— my dar-ling!
2. In the gloam-ing oh,— my dar-ling!

when the lights are dim and low, And the
think not bit-ter-ly of me! Though I

qui-et shad-ows, fall-ing, soft-ly come and
passed a-way— in si-lence, left you lone-ly,

SHINE ON, HARVEST MOON

Nora Bayes and Jack Norworth

When Nora Bayes introduced this song in Ziegfeld's "Follies of 1908" she was already, as vaudeville and musical comedy star, perhaps the most popular songstress of her time. It was said she could make a hit of any song she sang, and she did probably make as many hits as any other woman singer. But this one, which she wrote in collaboration with her husband "in real life," Jack Norworth, was the song inextricably associated with her for the rest of her life and its title was selected as the title of a film biography of Miss Bayes made many years later.

June or Ju-ly___ Snow time ain't no time to stay___ out-doors and spoon,___ So shine on, shine on har-vest moon for me and my gal.

THE ROSARY

ROBERT CAMERON ROGERS   ETHELBERT NEVIN

ETHELBERT NEVIN, born in Pittsburgh, has often been likened to Stephen C. Foster. Indeed, there are striking similarities in their lives and careers. Both encountered resistance from their families in becoming musicians. Both wrote mostly in miniature. Both died in their late thirties, Foster an alcoholic, Nevin a hopeless neurotic. Both wrote songs that are deathless masterpieces. THE ROSARY, written in 1896, is not a religious song, although Rogers' poem does create such a mood. It would be hard to name a song written in America that has exceeded it in popularity.

The hours I spent with thee, dear heart,

Are as a string of pearls to me;— I count them o-ver ev-'ry

one a-part, My ro-sa-ry, my ro-sa-ry!

Each hour a pearl, each pearl a pray'r,—

51

JEANIE, WITH THE LIGHT BROWN HAIR

STEPHEN C. FOSTER

STEPHEN FOSTER married Jane McDowell, the daughter of a Pittsburgh physician, in 1850. He was thinking of her when he wrote JEANIE, WITH THE LIGHT BROWN HAIR. After the Fosters' daughter was born, the songwriter-poet, though he seems never to have stopped loving his wife and daughter, proved ill adapted to domestic life. In the last unhappy years of his life, when he was separated from them, the words of this song were his favorites.

I dream of Jean - ie with the
I long for Jean - ie with the

light brown_ hair, Borne like a va - por,
day - dawn_ smile, Rad - iant in glad - ness,

on the sum - mer air; I see her trip-ping where the
warm with win - ning guile; I hear her mel - o - dies, like

bright streams play, Hap - py as the dai - sies that
joys gone_ by, Sigh - ing round my heart o'er the

SWEET GENEVIEVE

GEORGE COOPER   HENRY TUCKER

AFTER HIS association with Stephen C. Foster, the versatile Cooper collaborated with innumerable composers. He became very well known and successful, writing many popular songs, but in spite of his success he always needed money. He sold SWEET GENEVIEVE for five dollars, to Henry Tucker, who wrote the music. The poem had been written after the tragic death of Cooper's wife Genevieve, soon after their marriage. He never loved again.

1. Oh Gen-e-vieve, I'd give the world To live a-gain the love-ly past. The rose of youth was dew im-pearl'd But now it with-ers in the blast. I see thy face in ev-'ry dream; My wak-ing thoughts are

2. Fair Gen-e-vieve, my ear-ly love The years but make thee dear-er far. My heart shall nev-er, nev-er rove, Thou art my on-ly guid-ing star. For me the past has no re-gret; What-e'er the years may

full of thee. Thy glance is in the star-ry beam That
bring to me, I bless the hour when first we met, The

falls a - long the sum - mer sea.
hour that gave me love and thee.

CHORUS
Oh, Gen - e - vieve, Sweet Gen - e - vieve, The

days may come, the days may go, But still the hands of

mem - 'ry weave The bliss - ful dreams of long a - go.

I'LL TAKE YOU HOME AGAIN, KATHLEEN

Thomas P. Westendorf

This most Irish of songs was not written in Ireland, but in Plain-field, Indiana, by an American of German descent, who originally came from Virginia. He wrote it for his wife, to whom he was very devoted; but her name, Jennie, did not fit the music very well, so he used Kathleen instead. The song has been universally accepted as Irish.

I'll take you home a-gain, Kath-leen, A-cross the o-cean wild and wide, To where your heart has ev-er been, Since first you were my bon-nie bride. The ros-es all have left your cheek, I've watched them fade a-way and

die; Your voice is sad when-e'er you

speak, And tears be-dim your lov-ing eyes.

CHORUS

Oh! I will take you back a-gain, To

where your heart will feel no pain, And when the fields are fresh and

green, I'll— take you to your home a-gain.

MY WILD IRISH ROSE

CHAUNCEY OLCOTT

ALTHOUGH IT IS a "popular song" in every sense, this has many of the characteristics of the great folk songs. It has been sung by three generations of Americans and is known to almost everyone; many will be surprised to learn that it is not a genuine folk song. It was published in 1899, when recent heavy Irish immigration had created a demand for Irish songs; this was the first of the quasi-traditional ones and so is historic. Olcott, a matinee idol of that era, introduced the song in his own show.

My wild I - rish rose,_____ The

sweet - est flow'r that grows,_____ You may search ev - 'ry-

where, but none can com - pare With my wild I - rish

THE ROSE OF TRALEE

C. MORDAUNT SPENCER

CHARLES W. GLOVER

AN IRISH SONG with a sweet simplicity that is reminiscent of Thomas Moore, this long-time favorite came with the Irish to the New World. Glover himself was never in America, so far as is known, but many of his songs became popular here. Tralee is the county seat of County Kerry, Ireland.

1. The pale moon was ris-ing a-bove the green
2. The cool shades of eve-ning their man-tle were

moun-tain, The sun was de-clin-ing be-neath the blue
spread-ing, And Ma-ry, all smil-ing, was lis-t'ning to

sea, When I strayed with my love to the pure crys-tal
me; The— moon thro' the val-ley her pale rays was

foun-tain That stands in the beau-ti-ful vale of Tra-lee.
shed-ding,When I won the heart of the Rose of Tra-lee.

61

JUANITA

MRS. CAROLINE NORTON   *Spanish Melody*

SPANISH FOLK SONG is represented here, with its rhythmic three-four lilt. The early settlers of California sang it in their mother tongue, and Mrs. Norton's verse, in English, gave it a permanent place as one of America's favorites. Caroline Norton was a granddaughter of Richard Brinsley Sheridan, the Irish dramatist. All efforts to trace the composer have failed, and we must consider the melody a folk song. No song is more universally included in songbooks and collections, especially those intended for use in schools.

1. Soft o'er the foun-tain, Ling-'ring falls the
2. When in thy dream-ing, Moons like these shall

south-ern moon;   Far   o'er the   moun-tain,
shine a-gain,   And   day-light beam-ing

Breaks the day too soon!   In thy dark eye's
Prove thy dreams are vain,   Wilt thou not, re-

splen-dor, Where the warm light loves to dwell,
lent - ing, For thy ab-sent lov - er sigh,

Wea-ry looks, yet ten-der, Speak their fond fare-well!
In thy heart con-sent-ing To a pray'r gone by!

Ni - ta! Jua - ni-ta! Ask thy soul if
Ni - ta! Jua - ni-ta! Let me lin-ger

we should part! Ni-ta! Jua - ni-ta! Lean thou on my heart.
by thy side! Ni-ta! Jua - ni-ta! Be my own fair bride!

63

ANNIE LAURIE

WILLIAM DOUGLASS   LADY JOHN SCOTT

S. J. ADAIR FITZGERALD, the historian, tells of an old lady who heard ANNIE LAURIE sung in 1854. She was a descendant of Douglass of Fingland, and she said that he was desperately in love with Annie Laurie when he wrote the song, "but," she added, "he did na get her after all." Annie Laurie married the Ferguson of Craigdarrock, whose house, five miles away, could be seen from Maxwelton House, where she was born in 1682. Lady John Scott altered and polished the song, and possibly wrote the third verse.

1. Max - wel - ton's braes are bon - nie, Where ear - ly fa's the dew, And 'twas there that An - nie
2. Her brow is like the snow-drift, Her throat is like the swan; Her face, it is the
3. Like dew on th'gow - an ly - ing Is th' fa' o'her fair - y feet, And like winds in sum - mer

Lau - rie Gie'd me her prom - ise
fair - est That e'er the sun shone
sigh - ing, Her voice is low and

true; Gie'd me her prom - ise true, Which
on; That e'er the sun shone on, And
sweet; Her voice is low and sweet, And she's

ne'er for - got will be,
dark blue is her e'e, } And for bon - nie An - nie
a' the world to me,

Lau - rie, I'd lay me doon and dee.

SWEET ADELINE

Richard Gerard (R. G. Husch)   Harry Armstrong

This song, published in 1903 and the undisputed theme song of barbershop quartets for some forty years, is historic in at least three other ways: It pioneered the "repeat" or "echo" lyric (Sweet Adeline, my Adeline); it acquired, undeservedly, the stigma of being a "drunken" song; and it evidenced the irrational vagaries of public taste in matters of title. Originally titled *Down Home in Old New England*, it could not find a publisher. As *You're the Flower of My Heart, Sweet Rosalie*, it failed. With Rosalie changed to Adeline (in honor of Adelina Patti), it became an all-time hit.

Sweet A - del - ine (Sweet A - del - ine) My A - del-

ine (My A - del - ine) At night, dear

heart, (At night dear heart) For you I

DEAR OLD GIRL

Richard Henry Buck

Theodore F. Morse

THIS SONG IS A "MUST" for every male quartet. The lyricist, Buck, was among the best of his times; the composer, Morse, was one of the outstanding songwriters of the early years of this century. But of Morse's many successful songs, only this one has survived—making allowance for one odd exception. As David Ewen has pointed out, the one Morse production that *everyone* knows is the few words he added to a Gilbert and Sullivan march in *The Pirates of Penzance*: "Hail, hail, the gang's all here."

I LOVE YOU TRULY

CARRIE JACOBS BOND

THIS BEAUTIFUL SONG is known wherever English is spoken. It is almost a standard part of American wedding ceremonies, usually as a solo sung after the service. Mrs. Bond, who turned to songwriting when she was widowed, was the only woman on the original list of those rated AA (highest) when the American Society of Composers, Authors and Publishers (ASCAP) was formed. The General Federation of Women's Clubs placed her among the first fifty women of this century.

1. I love you tru-ly,___ tru-ly dear,
2. Ah, love 'tis some-thing to feel your kind hand,

Life with its sor-row,___ Life with its tear,___
Ah, yes, 'tis some-thing by your side to stand,—

Fades in-to dreams when I feel you are near,
Gone is the sor-row,___ Gone doubt and fear,

For I love you tru-ly, tru-ly dear.___
For you love me tru-ly, tru-ly dear.___

OH, PROMISE ME

CLEMENT SCOTT   REGINALD DeKoven

THE OPERETTA *Robin Hood*, of which OH, PROMISE ME is a part,
has been a permanent success, often revived; but if Scott and De-
Koven had never written anything but the one song, their fame
would have been assured. It has been sung so consistently at wed-
dings that it is treated almost as part of the service, in which
respect it has few competitors.

1. Oh, prom-ise me that some-day you and I Will
2. Oh, prom-ise me that you will take my hand, The

take our love to-geth-er to some sky Where
most un-worth-y in this lone-ly land, And

we can be a-lone, and faith re-new, And
let me sit be-side you, in your eyes,

find the hol - lows where those flow - ers grew,— Those
See - ing the vi - sion of our para - dise, —

first_ sweet_ vi - o - lets of ear - ly spring, Which
Hear - ing God's mes - sage while the or - gan rolls Its

come in whis - pers, thrill us both, and sing Of
might - y mu - sic to our ver - y souls; No

love un - speak - a - ble that is to be; }
love less per - fect than a life with thee; } Oh,

prom - ise me! Oh, prom - ise me!

BELIEVE ME, IF ALL THOSE ENDEARING YOUNG CHARMS

THOMAS MOORE   *Traditional*

MOST AUTHORITIES have said that the tune is English, *My Lodging Is On The Cold Ground*, but Edward Bunting insists that it is Irish, and points to the repeated use of the submediant, typical of Irish music. Moore, at any rate, wrote it to what he knew as "*As fada armso me* (Long am I here)." The alma mater of Harvard College, *Fair Harvard*, is sung to the same tune.

1. Be - lieve me, if all those en - dear - ing young charms, Which I gaze on so fond-ly to-day,— Were to change by to-mor-row and fleet in my arms, Like— fair - y gifts fad-ing a-

2. It___ is not while beau - ty and youth are thine own, And thy cheek un-pro-faned by a tear,— That the fer - vor and faith of a soul can be known, To which time will but make thee more

way,— Thou wouldst still be a-dored— as this
dear;— No, the heart that has tru-ly loved—

mo-ment thou art, Let thy love-li-ness fade as it
nev-er for-gets, But as tru-ly loves on to the

will;— And a-round the dear ru-in each
close;— As the sun-flow-er turns on her

wish of my heart Would en-twine it-self ver-dant-ly still.—
god, when he sets, The same look which she turn'd when he rose.—

LONG, LONG AGO

Thomas Haynes Bayly

THIS SONG, so widely known and loved, was published in London, in 1843, as *The Long Ago*. The original title was changed by the public and is no longer used or remembered. Bayly was a successful songwriter during his lifetime, but of his songs only LONG, LONG AGO has survived. He was a poet rather than a musician, and most of his songs were set to music by others; but this melody he wrote himself, and it has an indestructible quality that has furnished a basis for many, more ephemeral, popular songs.

1. Tell me the tales that to me were so dear,
2. Do you re-mem-ber the paths where we met,
3. Tho' by your kind-ness my fond hopes were raised,

Long, long a-go, Long, long a-go;
Sing me the songs I de-
Ah, yes, you told me you
You, by more el-o-quent

light-ed to hear,
ne'er would for-get,
lips have been praised,
Long, long a-go, long a-go.

Now you are come, all my grief is re-moved,
Then, to all oth-ers my smile you pre-ferr'd,
But by long ab-sence your truth has been tried,

Let me for-get that so long you have roved,
Love, when you spoke, gave a charm to each word,
Still to your ac-cents I lis-ten with pride,

Let me be-lieve that you love as you loved,
Still my heart treas-ures the prais-es I heard,
Blest as I was when I sat by your side,

Long, long a-go, long a-go.

SILVER THREADS AMONG THE GOL

Eben E. Rexford   Hart Pease Danks

REXFORD was the editor of a farmers' weekly, in which he some-times printed verses he had written. When Danks, a successful composer, seemed attracted, Rexford sold him a number of verses for three dollars. One of these was SILVER THREADS AMONG THE GOLD. It became one of the most successful songs of all time, but the composer, like Stephen Foster, died in a furnished room, separated from those he loved, and in dire want. He left unfinished something he had started to write: "It is hard to die alone and..."

1. Dar - ling, I am grow - ing old,____
2. Love can nev - er - more grow old,____

Sil - ver threads a - mong the gold
Locks may lose their brown and gold;

Shine up - on my brow to - day,____
Cheeks may fade and hol - low grow,____

76

WHEN YOU AND I WERE YOUNG, MAGGIE

GEORGE W. JOHNSON   JAMES AUSTIN BUTTERFIELD

"THIS SONG has a real story, which has become so garbled through the years that it should be straightened out once and for all," writes Sigmund Spaeth in *A History of Popular Music*. This is the story: Johnson was a Canadian schoolteacher. At a little mill by a creek in Canada, he used to meet one of his pupils, Maggie Clark. They were deeply in love, and in 1865 they were married and went to live in Cleveland, Ohio, where Johnson had taken a position as a teacher. But Maggie died the same year, and Johnson's poem proved to be only a dream of what might have been. Butterfield, a teacher of music, set Johnson's poem to music and it was published in 1866. The song, simple and unpretentious and full of sincerity, is loved by the whole world.

1. I wan-dered to-day to the hill, Mag-gie, To watch the scene be-low, The creek and the old rust-y mill, Mag-gie, Where we sat in the long, long a-go.

2. A cit-y so si-lent and lone, Mag-gie, Where the young and the gay and the best, In pol-ished white man-sions of stone, Mag-gie, Have each found a place of rest,

78

The green grove is gone from the
Is built where the birds used to
Chos. And now we are a ged and

hill, Mag - gie, Where first the_ dai - sies_
play, Mag - gie, And join in the songs that were
gray, Mag - gie, The tri - als of life near - ly

sprung;_ The_ old rust - y mill is_
sung,_ For we sang just as gay as_
done,_ But to me you're as fair as you

still, Mag - gie, Since you and_ I were_ young._
they, Mag - gie, When you and_ I were_ young._
were, Mag - gie, When you and_ I were_ young._

D. S. for Chorus

LOVE'S OLD SWEET SONG

C. CLIFTON BINGHAM   JAMES L. MOLLOY

THE FIRST PUBLICATION of this sweet song, with its ineffable nostalgic mood, was in England in 1884. Within a year it had swept the world, and this in a day before radio or phonograph records were available to create overnight saturation. Not too much is known about Bingham, but Molloy was a composer of wide scope, writing operettas and songs of considerable success. LOVE'S OLD SWEET SONG far overshadowed most other popular songs of the period, and probably set a new standard for songs of the type.

Once in the dear dead days be-yond re-call,

When on the world the mists be-gan to fall, Out of the dreams that

rose in hap-py throng, Low to our hearts love sang an old sweet song

And in the dusk, where fell the fire-light gleam,

Soft - ly it wove it - self in - to our dream.

CHORUS

Just a song at twi-light, when the lights are low,

And the flick-'ring shad-ows__ soft - ly come and go;__

Tho' the heart be wea-ry, sad the day and long, Still to us at

twi-light comes love's old song, Comes love's old sweet song.

WHEN YOU WERE SWEET SIXTEEN

JAMES THORNTON

JIM THORNTON was a vaudevillian, teamed with Charles Lawlor. Jim's wife Bonnie became a famous singer and helped to popularize his songs. Many of these were great successes in their time, but all are forgotten except WHEN YOU WERE SWEET SIXTEEN, written in 1898. It is said that Bonnie always waited at the stagedoor on payday to commandeer her husband's salary before he could spend it on liquor. Thornton "took the cure" several times, with complete failure. Then he simply stopped drinking. WHEN YOU WERE SWEET SIXTEEN was revived in 1944 and reached the position of No. 1 in nationwide popularity.

I love you, as I ne-ver loved be-fore,_____ Since first I met you on the vil - lage green;_____ Come to me, or my dream of love is o'er,_____ I love you as I loved you_____ When you were sweet _____ When you were sweet _____ Six - teen._____

(when you were sweet,)

(when you were sweet,)

LOCH LOMOND

ANONYMOUS

LOCH LOMOND lies between the counties of Dumbarton and Stirling, in Scotland, and not far from the city of Glasgow. Not much is known about the song. Early Scottish editions bore the credit line, "By a lady," and the wide variety of scales found in the folk music of the Scots makes it very difficult to place it in a specific period. It may be of comparatively recent origin, or quite ancient.

1. By yon bon-nie banks, And by yon bon-nie braes, Where the sun shines bright on Loch Lo-mond, Where me and my true love were ev-er wont to gae On the

2. 'Twas then that we part-ed In yon sha-dy glen On the steep, steep side of Ben Lo-mond, Where in pur-ple hue— the High-land hills we view And the

3. The wee bird-ies sing And the wild flowers spring, And in sun-shine the wa-ters are sleep-ing, But the bro-ken heart it kens— Nae sec-ond Spring again Though the

84

ALL THROUGH THE NIGHT

Attributed to DAVID OWEN   *Welsh air: Ar Hyd y Nos*

THE PEOPLE of Wales, with their long tradition of group singing, have given us this, one of the most beautiful of their folk songs. An English version beginning:

> "Here beneath a willow weepeth
> Poor Mary Ann"

was written by Mrs. Constance Opie. The tune is ancient and of unknown origin.

1. Sleep, my child, and peace at-tend thee,
2. While the moon her watch is keep-ing

All through the night,   Guard-ian an-gels
All through the night,   While the wea-ry

God will send thee, All through the night;
world is sleep-ing, All through the night;

Soft the drow-sy hours are creep-ing, Hill and vale in
O'er thy spir-it gen-tly steal-ing, Vi-sions of de-

slum - ber steep-ing, I my lov-ing
light re - veal-ing, Breathes a pure and

vig - il keep-ing All through the night.
ho - ly feel-ing All through the night.

SWEET AND LOW

ALFRED TENNYSON

JOSEPH BARNBY

JOSEPH BARNBY was a musical prodigy, and later became conductor of the Albert Hall Choral Society, succeeding Gounod in 1871. He wrote hundreds of hymns and four-part songs, his harmonizations being distinctive and well in advance of his time. He was knighted in 1892. The poem is one of the several lyrics, by some considered Tennyson's best, in *The Princess*.

1. Sweet and low, sweet and low, Wind of the west-ern sea;— Low, low,— breathe and blow, Wind of the west-ern sea;—
2. Sleep and rest, sleep and rest, Fa-ther will come to thee soon;— Rest, rest on moth-er's breast, Fa-ther will come to thee soon;—

O - ver the roll - ing wa - ters go,
O - ver the wa - ters go,
Fa-ther will come to his babe in the nest,
Fa - ther will come to his babe,

Come from the dy - ing moon, and blow,
Come ____ from _ the moon _ and blow,
Sil - ver sails all out of the west,
Sil - ver sails out of _ the west,

Blow him a-gain to me,— While my lit-tle one,
Un-der the sil - ver moon,— Sleep, my lit-tle one,

while my pret - ty one sleeps.____
sleep my pret - ty one, sleep.____

CRADLE SONG
(Wiegenlied)

German from
Des Knaben Wunderhorn　　　　　　　　　　　　JOHANNES BRAHMS

THIS LITTLE SONG is also known as "Brahms' Lullaby." It was published by Karl Simrock, of Berlin, in 1868, and reached America the same year, being No. 4 in Brahms' *Fünf Lieder,* Opus 49. Much of the lyric so clearly suggests an English equivalent that several English versions, independently produced, are almost word-for-word the same. Mrs. Natalia Macfarren's English version was the first to have circulation in America.

Lul - la - by and good-
Gu - ten A - bend, gut'

night, with ros-es be-dight,_ With_
*Nacht, mit Ro-sen be-dacht,_ Mit_*

flow-ers round thy head, Be thou co-zy in thy
Nelk-lein be-deckt schlupf' un-ter die

90

bed.   Lay thee down now and   rest, May thy
Deck'; Mor - gen früh, wenn Gott   will, wirst du

slum-bers be   blest;   Lay thee down now and
wie - der   ge - weckt;   Mor - gen   früh, wenn Gott

rest,   May thy   slum - bers   be   blest.
will,   wirst   du   wie - der   ge - weckt.

SONGS MY MOTHER TAUGHT ME

English: NATALIA MACFARREN
German: ADOLPH HEYDUK

ANTON DVORÂK

THIS SONG, by the great Bohemian composer of the symphony *From the New World*, has a place on the concert stage and also in the repertoire of every quartet and glee club. It has the sentimental appeal of a popular song, and in her translation, Mrs. Macfarren has captured the poetry of the original German text. The song was published in America in 1880, before Dvorâk's stay in the United States.

Songs my mother taught me, In the days long
Als die al-te Mut-ter mich noch lehr-te

van - ished; Sel-dom from her eye - lids
sin - gen, trä-nen in den Wim - pern

Were the tear-drops ban - ished. Now I teach my
gar so oft ihr hin - gen. Jetzt, wo ich die

chil - dren Each mel - o - dious meas - ure.
Klei - nen sel - ber üb im San - ge,

Oft the tears are flow - ing, Oft they flow
rie-selt's in den Bart oft, rie-selt's oft

from my mem - 'ry's treas - ure.
von der brau - nen Wan - ge.

AULD LANG SYNE

ROBERT BURNS

Attributed to
WILLIAM SHIELD

AULD LANG SYNE is a *strathspey*, a dance from the region of Spey, in Scotland. Burns adapted the traditional words and William Shield used the tune in one of his operas. The form in which we now know the song has become an institution for New Year's Eve. *Bohunkus*, using the same tune, has always been popular in collegiate circles, and Princeton used the tune for *Old Nassau*.

1. Should auld ac-quaint-ance
2. We twa hae paid-l't
3. And there's a hand, my

be for-got, And nev-er brought to
i' the burn, From morn-in' sun to
trust-y fier, And gie's a hand o'

min'? Should auld ac-quaint-ance
dine; But seas be-tween us
thine; And we'll tak a right guid-

PAIDL'T, paddled   FIER, friend   WILLIE WAUGHT, friendly draught
BURN, brook

HOME SWEET HOME

JOHN HOWARD PAYNE   SIR HENRY ROWLEY BISHOP

BOTH ENGLAND AND AMERICA can justly claim this song, for it was written jointly by Payne, an American, and Bishop, who was conductor of the London Philharmonic Society in 1814. Payne was a vagabond of sorts, and it has been said that "the man who wrote HOME SWEET HOME never had a home of his own." This is not far from true, but when Payne died he was representing his country as consul to Tunis. The tune, which Bishop had included in a collection as *Sicilian Air,* was assumed by others to be a folk song. It was only through a legal investigation that he proved his claim as composer. The complete song first appeared in London, in 1823, as part of an opera, *The Maid of Milan.*

1. 'Mid pleasures and palaces though we may roam, Be it ever so humble There's no place like home. A
2. An exile from home splendor dazzles in vain; Oh, give me my lowly thatched cottage again. The

charm from the skies seems to hal-low us there, Which,
birds sing-ing gai-ly that come at my call, Give me

seek through the world, is not met with else-
them with that peace of mind dear-er than

where. Home! home! sweet, sweet home!
all. Home! home! sweet, sweet home!

There's no place like home, Oh, there's no place like home.

MY OLD KENTUCKY HOME, GOODNIGHT

STEPHEN C. FOSTER

KENTUCKY has made this its state song, and there is a state shrine at Bardstown, Ky., where Foster's relatives, the Rowans, lived, and where the song was believed to have been written; but the investigations of John Tasker Howard have shown that Foster wrote the song while on tour, and may never have been in Kentucky. The great success of Mrs. Stowe's *Uncle Tom's Cabin*, with its Kentucky setting, undoubtedly inspired this song and its title; the song, like the book, was published in 1852.

1. The sun shines bright in the old Ken-tuck-y home, 'Tis
   young folks roll on the lit-tle cab-in floor, All
2. They hunt no more for the 'pos-sum and the coon, On the
   day goes by like a shad-ow o'er the heart, With
3. The head must bow and the back will have to bend, Wher-
   few more days for to tote the wea-ry load, No

sum-mer, we're care-free and gay; The
mer-ry, all hap-py and bright; By'n
mead-ow, the hill and the shore; They
sor-row where all was de-light; The
ev-er we ev-er may go; A
mat-ter, 'twill nev-er be light; A

corn-top's ripe and the mead-ow's in the bloom, While the
by hard times comes a-knock-ing at the door, Then my
sing no more by the glim-mer of the moon, On the
time has come when we know we have to part, Then my
few more days, and the trou-ble all will end, In the
few more days till we tot-ter on the road, Then my

1. birds make music all the day; The
2. bench by the old cabin door; The
3. field where the su-gar-canes grow; A

old Ken-tuck-y home, good-night!
old Ken-tuck-y home, good-night!
old Ken-tuck-y home, good-night!

CHORUS

Weep no more my la-dy, Oh, weep no more to-

day! We will sing one song for the old Ken-tuck-y home, for the

old Ken-tuck-y home far a-way.

THE OLD FOLKS AT HOME
(Swanee River)

STEPHEN C. FOSTER

FOSTER wanted a good two-syllable name for a southern river, to finish a song. He consulted his brother, who produced an atlas and began to look at the maps. Stephen waited, and finally his brother said:

"How about this one? Suwannee River?"

Thus the song was finished, in 1851, and became Foster's most successful work. But he spelled the name wrong, "Swanee," and so it has remained. The real river is the Suwannee, in Florida, which empties into the Gulf of Mexico.

1. 'Way down up-on the Swa-nee Riv-er, Far, far a-way, There's where my heart is turn-ing ev-er, There's where the old folks stay. All up and down the

2. All 'round the lit-tle farm I wan-dered, When I was young; Then man-y hap-py days I squan-dered, Man-y the songs I sung. When I was play-ing

3. One lit-tle hut a-mong the bush-es, One that I love, Still sad-ly to my mem-'ry rush-es, No mat-ter where I rove. When will I see the

whole cre - a - tion, Sad - ly I roam, Still long-ing for the
with my broth - er, Hap - py was I; Oh, take me to my
bees a - hum-ming All 'round the comb? When will I hear the

old plan - ta - tion, And for the old folks at home.
kind old moth - er, There let me live and__ die.
ban - jo tum-ming, Down in my good old__ home?

CHORUS

All the world is sad and drear-y, Ev'-ry-where I roam;

Oh! la-dies, how my heart grows wea-ry, Far from the old folks at home.

ON THE BANKS OF THE WABASH

PAUL DRESSER

THIS IS THE OFFICIAL SONG of the State of Indiana. Dresser, a giant in size (300+ pounds) and a giant in songwriting in his times, wrote both words and music, notwithstanding reports that his more famous younger brother, novelist Theodore Dreiser, helped him. Dreiser was the original name, which Paul simplified. Though Paul Dresser wrote hundreds of songs, of which some dozens were hits, he died penniless. This song, the chief survivor, deserves its immortality if only for its simple nostalgic appeal.

Oh, The moon-light's fair to-night a-long the Wa-bash,___ From the fields there comes the breath of new mown hay___ Thru the syc-a-mores the can-dle lights are gleam-ing,___ On the Banks of the Wa-bash, far a-way. (Far a-way.)

WAIT TILL THE SUN SHINES, NELLIE

Andrew B. Sterling   Harry von Tilzer

THE SIMPLICITY and harmonic construction of this song have long established it in the repertory of all barbershop quartets, most of whose members probably believe it older than it is (1905). Harry von Tilzer (born Harry Gumm) perhaps wrote more neo- and quasi-folksongs than any other American songwriter. Sterling wrote the words for many of the standard songs of the early 1900s. In 1906, when the San Francisco disaster occurred, "Frisco" was often substituted for "Nellie" in singing this song.

Wait till the sun shines, Nel-lie, And the clouds go drift-ing by We'll be so hap-py Nel-lie Don't you cry Down lov-ers' lane we'll wan-der, sweet-heart you and I, Wait till the sun shines, Nel-lie Bye and Bye.

DAISY BELL
(On A Bicycle Built for Two)

HARRY DACRE

WHEN HARRY DACRE came to America from England there was already a wave of bicycle songs in progress, and the bicycle "built for two," the tandem bike, was to be seen everywhere. Dacre was unacqainted with the New York publishers (though he had written successful songs in England) and could not place his song, written in 1892. Katie Lawrence, an English singer, introduced it in London, and it became immediately and permanently popular. For community sings it is sure to be included, and as it was written in the 'nineties, at the height of the bicycle craze, there is no better musical theme for that period.

Dai - sy, Dai - sy, Give me your an - swer, do!___ I'm half cra - zy, All for the love of you!___ It

won't be a styl-ish mar-riage,—

I can't af-ford a car-riage,—

But you'll look sweet, Up-on the

seat of a bi-cy-cle built for two!—

AFTER THE BALL

CHARLES K. HARRIS

MANY WRITERS might have been discouraged after a first performance such as befell AFTER THE BALL, when the singer forgot the words. But Harris believed in his song, and when no publisher seemed interested he published it himself, a fact later regretted by every publisher to whom Harris had offered it. A famous singer, J. Aldrich Libby, introduced it in the revue *A Trip to Chinatown*, and it was featured by John Philip Sousa at the Chicago World's Fair in 1893. Sales exceeded five million copies, placing the song among the most popular of all time.

Af- ter the ball is o - ver,

Af - ter the break of morn,——

Af - ter the danc- ers' leav - ing,

After the stars are gone;____ Man-y a heart is ach - ing, If you could read them all:____ Man - y the hopes that have van - ished, Af - ter the ball.____

107

THE BAND PLAYED ON

JOHN E. PALMER

CHARLES B. WARD
JOHN E. PALMER

THE SONG about "Casey and the Strawberry Blonde" was the subject of a newspaper promotion in 1895, when the New York *World* gave it a publicity campaign. Charles B. Ward wrote no fewer than four songs in which the word "band" appeared in the title; but both words and music of THE BAND PLAYED ON were written by Palmer. Ward bought it outright, "doctored" it and published it himself. In 1946 a motion picture was founded upon the song.

Ca-sey would waltz with the straw-ber-ry blonde, And the Band Played On, _____ He'd glide o'er the (Played on,) floor with the girl he a-dored, And the Band Played

On,_____ But his brain was so load-ed he

(and on)

near-ly ex plod-ed, The poor girl would shake with a-

larm,_____ He mar-ried the girl with the

(a - larm)

straw-ber-ry curls, And the Band Played On._____

THE SIDEWALKS OF NEW YORK
(East Side, West Side)

JAMES W. BLAKE   CHARLES B. LAWLOR

CHARLES B. LAWLOR (vaudeville partner of Jim Thornton, who wrote *When You Were Sweet Sixteen*) was in the store where Blake worked as a hat salesman. Lawlor hummed his new tune for Blake, who wrote down the words while on the job. This was in 1894, and ever since there has been no other musical signature for New York, and to some extent big cities in general. Alfred E. Smith used it as a theme song during his presidential campaign in 1928.

East side, West side, all a-round the town,— The tots play "Ring-a-ros-ie," "Lon-don Bridge is fall-ing

110

down!"— Boys and girls to-
to-

gether,— Me and Ma-mie Rorke,— We
geth - er,

trip the light_ fan - tas-tic on the

side-walks of New York.—

THE MAN ON THE FLYING TRAPEZE

GEORGE LEYBOURNE   **ALFRED LEE**

WHEN THIS FAMOUS SONG was first published, it was by three differ-ent publishers, all in 1868. None of them credited the writers, and it was some years later that they were recognized. Some collections, even dated in the 1950s, failed to credit the writers, perpetuating the omission. The song was revived through its use in the motion picture *It Happened One Night*, the outstanding film of 1934.

1. Oh,___ once I was hap-py but now I'm for-lorn,___ Like an old coat that is tat-ter'd and torn.___ Left in this wide world to fret and to
2. Now the young man by name was Señ- or Bon-i Slang,___ Tall, big and hand-some, as well made as Chang. When-e'er he ap-peared___ the
3. Some___ months af-ter that I went in-to a hall,___ To my sur-prise I found there on the wall A bill in red let-ters that
Chorus: He___ flies thro' the air with the great-est of ease, This dar-ing young man on the fly-ing tra-peze, His move-ments are grace-ful; all
Last Chorus: She___ floats thro' the air with the great-est of ease, You'd think her a man on the fly-ing tra-peze, She does all the work___ while

LITTLE BROWN JUG

Attributed to
JOSEPH E. WINNER

THIS SONG has been called "the wettest ever written," which is undoubtedly true. It is perhaps for that reason that Winner, who probably wrote both words and music in 1869, published it under the name of Eastburn. At that time were gathering the temperance forces that later were to become an organized movement (W.C.T.U.). We can guess that Winner, using excellent judgment, played it safe.

115

JINGLE BELLS

J. S. PIERPONT

IF EVER A SONG could turn back time to the days before the automobile and the super-highway, it would be this one. Even the youngest can experience a sleigh-ride through the magic of this music. Written in 1857, it has been a winter "standard" ever since; and who, hearing it played, can resist the impulse to tap on his glass? Sleigh-bells were placed upon the horses as a warning, for otherwise the approaching sleigh made hardly a sound.

Dash - ing thro' the snow In a
one horse o - pen sleigh, O'er the fields we go,
Laugh-ing all the way; Bells on bob - tail ring,
Mak-ing spir - its bright; What fun it is to ride and sing a

ALOHA OE

QUEEN LYDIA LILIUOKALANI

ALOHA OE is not the national anthem of the Hawaiian Islands, but it has become so well known to the rest of the world that it is the song heard for gatherings and festivities not affairs of state. When a steamer docks at Honolulu the band is there to play ALOHA OE, and when the visitor departs it is to the same strain. *Aloha*, in the Hawaiian language, means farewell, or love, or greeting, or just best wishes; and also it has meanings that cannot be expressed in any other language. Liliuokalani wrote it in 1878, partly in Hawaiian and partly in English. The melody is similar to that of an earlier song, *The Rock Beside the Sea*, by Charles Converse, but that may be coincidence.

Proud-ly swept the rain cloud by the
Ha - a - heo e ka u - a i - na

cliff,__ As on__ it glid-ed__through the
pa - li, Ke ni - hi a - e - la i - ka - na

trees,__ Still__ fol-low-ing with grief our
he - le, E ha - ha - i a - na i - ka

love song, Borne to sea with the flow-ers on the
li - ko, Pu-a a-hi-hi le-hu-a o

breeze._ Fare-well to thee, fare-well to thee! Thou
u - ka A - lo-ha oe, A - lo-ha oe, E ke

charm-ing one who dwells a-mong the bow-ers; One
o - na-o-na no-ho i - ka li - po; One

fond embrace before I now depart, Un-til we meet a-gain.
fond embrace, a-ho-i a - e au, Un-til we meet a-gain.

119

LA PALOMA

Sebastian Yradier

Yradier published most of his songs in Paris, where he served as singing master to the Empress Eugenie. He was a Spaniard and his songs were of typical Spanish color; Bizet, believing that his *El Areglito* was a folk song, used the theme for the Habanera in *Carmen*. La Paloma was published in the United States in 1877. All attempts to trace the author of the beautiful English words have been to no avail.

CIELITO LINDO

English version by
JAMES MOREHEAD   CARLOS FERNANDEZ

THIS MAGNIFICENT SONG was popular in California through its tenancy by Spain and Mexico. It remained very popular among Spanish-speaking peoples, and then suddenly, in 1923, became a "hit" song in the United States. A pattern of syncopation that is not exactly like that of any other song, and an engaging lilt, assure it permanent popularity. All along the Mexican border there are hundreds of people who know the words of CIELITO LINDO in Spanish, even though they do not speak a word of the language and have no idea what they are singing.

Moun-tains high_ seem to   hide the sky_
De la Sie - rra Mo - re - na, Cie-

_ When the clouds hang low_ on the ceil-ing;_
li - to Lin - do, vie_ nen ba-jan-do,_

Nev - er mind,_ for it's clear be - hind,_
Un par de_o - ji - tos ne - gros Cie-

LA CUCARACHA

Mexican Folk Song

LA CUCARACHA (the cockroach) in Mexico is idiomatically applied to an old maid. During the Mexican Revolution of 1914-1917, the dictator Venustiano Carranza was so called by the forces of the revolutionists Pancho Villa and Emiliano Zapata. The song (based upon an ancient Spanish folk song) consists of a series of "dichos," or epigrammatic quatrains of folk origin and development, and includes allusions to Mexican political history. The English words, of unknown origin, are not easy to sing and do not rhyme, but they do constitute a translation.

Cuan - do   u - no   quie - re_a   u - na,
1. When   a   fel low   loves   a   maid - en
2. All   the   girls   from   Mex - i - co
3. One   thing   makes   me   laugh most heart - y:
4. Fel - low   needs   an   au - to - mo - bile

Y es - ta   u - na   no   lo   quie - re,
And   that   maid - en   does - n't   love   him,
Are   as   pret - ty   as   a   flow - er,
Pan - cho   Vi - lla   with   no   shirt   on;
If   he   un - der - takes   the   jour - ney

Es   lo   mis - mo   que   si_un   cal - vo
It's   the   same   as   when   a   bald   man
And   they   talk   so   ver - y   sweet - ly,
Now   the   Car - ran - zis - tas   "beat   it,"
To   the   place   at   which   Za - pa - ta

En la calle en-cuen-tra un pei - ne.
Finds a comb up - on the high - way.
Fill your heart quite up with love.
Be - cause Vi - lla's men are com - ing.
Or - dered the fa - mous con - ven - tion.

CHORUS

La cu - ca - ra - cha, La cu - ca - ra - cha,
The cu - ca - ra - cha, The cu - ca - ra - cha,

Ya no quie - re ca - mi - nar,— Por - que no
Does - n't want to trav - el on,— Be - cause she

tie - ne, Por - que le fal - ta,
has - n't, Oh, no, she has - n't

Ma - ri - hua - na que fu - mar.
Ma - ri - hua - na for to smoke.

THE LORELEI

Heinrich Heine
Translated by James Morehead

Friedrich Silcher

Heine captured the mood of an old German myth with such perfection that it found universal acceptance. Silcher, a composer who spent many years as musical director of the University of Tübingen, in Germany, in 1852 produced an ideal complement of Heine's poem. It is strophic in form, and has often been erroneously considered a folk song. The English translation by Emma Lazarus is faithful but not "singable"; in the English version used here the essentials of the story are told in two stanzas.

1. Oh, tell me the rea-son I sor-row, While
2. The Lor - e - lei, combing her tress-es That
1. Ich weiss nicht was soll es be - deu - ten, Dass

tear-drops glist in my eye? From whence the sad leg-end I
dim the gold of the comb Her song of the sir-en ad-
ich so trau - rig bin; Ein Mär-chen aus al - ten

bor - row, The tale of the Lor - e - lei? Then
dress - es Each boat seek-ing ha-ven and home. En-
zei - ten, Das kommt mir nicht aus dem Sinn. Die

lis - ten, while soft - ly   the Rhine flows, And
tranced by her voice sweet - ly   call - ing, They
Luft__ ist kühl und es   dun - kelt, Und

wea - ry birds seek their   rest;___   In
heed not the wind nor the   wave;___   But
ru - hig fliesst der   Rhein;___ Der

glo - ry, the sun in the sky_ glows, And
soon are in treach - er - y fall - ing To
Gi - pfel des Ber - ges fun - kelt Im

sinks__ a - way in the   west.__
death in a wa - ter - y   grave.__
A - bend - son - nen - schein.__

127

DARK EYES
(Otchi Tchorniya)

English version by
ALBERT MOREHEAD

ANONYMOUS

THIS RUSSIAN FOLK SONG probably originated in Spain in the 16th century or earlier, and was introduced into Russia by the gypsies who wandered through Spain, Hungary, and the Balkans. OTCHI TCHORNIYA is now a great favorite in America. The Russian words here given are those commonly sung by Russian-speaking Americans. The transliteration is by Princess Alexandra Kropotkin.

Eyes of dark-est hue,___
O - tchi tchor - ni - ya,___

Eyes where beau - ty lies,___
O - tchi yas - ni - ya,___

Eyes where pas-sion burns,__ Love-ly,
O - tchi jgut - chi - ya,____ E pre-

128

love - ly eyes!__ And I love you so,__
kras - ni - ya!__ Kak lu - blu ya vas,__

__ Yet I fear you too,__ For my
__ Kak bo - yus ya vas,__ Znat ou -

heart was lost__ When I first saw you.__
vi - del vas__ Ya v'ne - do - bry tchas.__

O SOLE MIO

Translated by
JAMES MOREHEAD

EDUARDO DI CAPUA

AMONG AMERICANS of Italian descent particularly, and among all generally, O SOLE MIO remains in high favor. The moving and climatic "Ma n'a—tu sole," at the start of the chorus, is most effective vocally, lending itself perfectly to the Neapolitan tenor timbre. Di Capua wrote many other songs which enjoy permanent popularity, both in Italy and America. The tune, with a new sentimental lyric *(There's No Tomorrow),* was a popular song of 1951.

What is more love-ly than a day of
Neapolitan: Che bel-la co-sa 'na iur na ta'e

sun-shine, ___ When clouds have passed a-way ___ and all the
so-le, ___ N'a-ria se-re-na dop-po 'na tem-

flow'rs are gay? ___ Just as the sun-shine
pe-sta, ___ Pe' ll'a-ria fre-sca

warms the sum-mer ros-es, ___ Bathed in your
pa-re gia' 'na fe-sta, ___ Che bel-la

won-d'rous love my heart re-pos-es.
co - sa 'na iur - na - ta'e so - le!

CHORUS *a tempo*

You are my sun-shine,— my light, my love!—
Ma n'a - tu so - le — cchiu bel lo ohi ne',

Your eyes re-cap-ture— the skies a-bove,—
'O so - le mi - o sta 'n fron - te a te!

And fill— my soul with rap - ture,
'O so - le'o so - le mi - o

My love-ly sun-shine,— my light, my love!—
sta 'n fron-te'a te, sta 'n fron-te a te!

SANTA LUCIA

Teodoro Cottrau

When Teodoro Cottrau wrote his gentle melody, he must have envisioned the beautiful Bay of Naples, his "home of fair poesy." A natural duet, Santa Lucia has always been an international favorite, both vocally and instrumentally. It is a *barcarolla*, or boatman's song, and typically Italian. The first edition was dated 1849, in Naples.

Now 'neath the sil-ver moon
Here balm-y zeph-yrs blow,
(Neapolitan) *Sul ma-re luc-ci-ca*

O-cean is glow-ing, O'er the calm
Pure joys in-vite us, And as we
l'a-stro d'ar-gen-to, pla-ci-da é

bil-low Soft winds are blow-ing.
gen-tly row All things de-light us.
l'on-da, pro-spero é il ven-to.

132

Hark, how the sail-or's cry Joy - ous - ly
Home of fair Po - e - sy, Realm of pure
Ve - ni-te al - l'agi - le bar-chet - ta

ech-oes nigh. San - ta__ Lu - ci - a!
Har-mo - ny, San - ta__ Lu - ci - a!
mi - a San-ta__ Lu - ci - a!

1.
San-ta Lu - ci - a!
San-ta Lu - ci - a!

2.
San-ta Lu - ci - a!
San-ta Lu - ci - a!

AU CLAIR DE LA LUNE

AUTHOR UNKNOWN
Translated by "C. F. M."

JEAN-BAPTISTE LULLY

LULLY, who died in Paris in 1687, is known as the founder of French Grand Opera. He was a musical giant who can be compared with Gluck and Wagner; he was a director, composer, stage-manager; he composed ballets, masques, symphonies, masses, choral works; he was a man of tremendous energy. But had he written nothing except AU CLAIR DE LA LUNE, his fame would have been assured. Little children never fail to learn it, along with their ABCs.

1. "At thy door I'm knock - ing,
2. Pier - rot cried in an - swer
1. Au clair de la lu - ne,
2. Au clair de la lu - ne,

By the pale moon-light, Lend a pen, I
By the pale moon-light, "In my bed I'm
Mon a - mi Pier - rot; Prê - te - moi ta
Pier - rot ré - pon - dit: "Je n'ai pas de

pray thee, I've a word to write;
ly - ing, Late and chill the night;
plu - me, Pour é - crire un mot.
plu - me, Je suis dans mon lit.

Chords: F · C7 · F · C7 · F7 · Bb · F7 · Bb · F7 · Bb

Gut - ter'd is my can - dle,___
Yon - der at my neigh - bor's___
Ma chan - delle est mor - te,___
Va chez la voi - si - ne,___

Burns my fire no more,   For the love of
Some-one is a - stir;   Fire is fresh - ly
Je n'ai plus de feu;   Ou - vre moi ta
Je crois qu'elle y est   Car dans sa cui-

heav - en,   O - pen now the door!"
kin - dled,   Get a light from her.
por - te,   Pour l'a - mour de Dieu.
si - ne   On bat le bri - quet."

ALOUETTE
(Gentle Skylark)

French-Canadian Folk Song

No "GANG" SONG has more appeal than this one, attested to by the fact that people sing it out lustily even when they have no idea what the words mean. It has been a long-time favorite in Canada, and spread all over the United States, to England, France, and probably everywhere else. An American version, in 1931, became nationally popular.

A - lou - et - te, gen - tille A - lou -
et - te, A - lou - et - te, je te plu - me - rai. rai.

Je te plu - me - rai la tête, Je te plu - me - rai la tête. Et la
2. le cou, Je te plu - me - rai le cou.
3. les ailes, Je te plu - me - rai les ailes.
4. les pattes, Je te plu - me - rai les pattes.
5. le dos, Je te plu - me - rai le dos.
6. la queue, Je te plu - me - rai la queue.

tête, Et la tête! A - lou - ette, A - lou - ette! Ah!

SEA, WESTERN AND FOLK SONGS

A LIFE ON THE OCEAN WAVE

EPES SARGENT   HENRY RUSSELL

EPES SARGENT wrote the words in 1838 after a stroll on the Battery, in New York City, and took the manuscript to his publisher. "This is not a song at all," said the publisher, and he turned it down. But Sargent's friend Henry Russell was of a different opinion. A few days later he wrote the lively tune that ever since has kept the song in permanent popularity. It was a favorite of the Hutchinsons, a famous band of family singers.

1. A life on the o - cean wave, A
2. Once more on the deck I stand Of my
3. The land is no long-er in view, The

home on the roll-ing deep, Where the
own swift-glid-ing craft, Set
clouds have be-gun to frown, But

scat - tered wa - ters rave, And the
sail! fare - well to the land, The
with a stout ves-sel and crew We'll

BLOW THE MAN DOWN

ANONYMOUS

WHEN A SAILING SHIP weighs anchor, every man in the crew is affected by the excitement of departure. Sails are set, and the pull on the halyards finds the sailors singing to a lively rhythm. This is one of the best known of the chanteys. It was originally called the *Black Ball Liner Song*. The Black Ball Line was a line of packets sailing between New York and Liverpool, and this chantey was sung in heavy hauling. BLOW THE MAN DOWN has always been directly identified with "Jack Tar," as between the lines we can hear the boast of the professional seaman, who recognizes in his mate singing and working beside him a brother sailor, a man like himself.

SOLO

1. Come all ye young fellows that follow the
2. 'Twas on a Black Baller I first served my
3. With the tinkers and tailors and soldiers and

CHORUS

sea,
time, To me way - hay, Blow the man down! {And
all,   {And
                                                                   {That

pay some attention and listen to me,)
in the Black Baller I wasted my prime, Oh,
ship for good sailors aboard a Black Ball,)

CHORUS

give me some time to blow the man down!

4. 'Tis when a Black Baller's preparing for sea,
To me way-hay, blow the man down!
You'd split your sides laughing, the sights you would see,
Oh, give me some time to blow the man down.

5. 'Tis when a Black Baller is clear of the land,
To me way-hay, blow the man down!
The crew musters aft at the word of command,
Oh, give me some time to blow the man down!

6. 'Tis larboard and starboard, on the deck you will sprawl,
To me way-hay, blow the man down!
For 'Kicking Jack Williams' commands the Black Ball,
Oh, give me some time to blow the man down!

The BLACK BALL LINE was a famous line of packets between New York and Liverpool.

NANCY LEE

FREDERICK E. WEATHERLY   STEPHEN ADAMS

A ROLLICKING and joyous ditty, NANCY LEE has always been a favorite with school children, even before they grasp the metaphorical "guiding star" of the sailor in the song. Weatherly and Adams (whose real name was Michael Myabrick) also wrote the famous sacred song *The Holy City*. NANCY LEE appeared in *Gems of English Song*, a collection published in Boston in 1875; but the song may be older.

Of all the wives as e'er you know, Yeo-ho! lads, ho! Yeo-ho! yeo-ho! There's none like Nan-cy Lee, I trow, Yeo-ho! lads, ho! yeo-ho! See there she stands and waves her hands, up-on the quay, An' ev-'ry day when

143

MY BONNIE LIES OVER THE OCEAN

ANONYMOUS

SIGMUND SPAETH says: "If people cannot be persuaded to sing *My Bonnie*, particularly when on the water, there is really no hope for them." Originally the jumps, or intervals, on "Bring back" went downward instead of upward. People didn't like it that way, and changed it, as is their prerogative with a folk song.

1. My Bon - nie lies o - ver the o - cean,— My Bon - nie lies o - ver the sea,— My Bon - nie lies o - ver the

2. Last night as I lay on my pil - low,— Last night as I lay on my bed,— Last night as I lay on my

3. O blow, ye winds, o - ver the o - cean, And blow ye winds o - ver the sea,— O blow, ye winds, o - ver the

145

HOME ON THE RANGE

Cowboy Song

JOHN A. LOMAX called this song "the cowboy's national anthem," and when it became known that it was the favorite of Franklin D. Roosevelt, the song became a "hit." Several claimants to a copyright on it immediately appeared. Some claims seemed well documented, and in one case a $500,000 lawsuit was instituted against publishers and recording companies. The matter at length reached the United States Senate and in at least one instance the controversy was recorded in the Congressional Record, but indisputably several versions are in the public domain.

1. Oh, give me a home, where the buf-fa-lo roam, Where the deer and the an-te-lope play;_ Where sel-dom is heard a dis-
2. How of-ten at night when the heav-ens are bright With the lights from the glit-ter-ing stars,_ Have I stood there a-mazed and_
3. Oh, give me a land where the bright dia-mond sand Flows_ lei-sure-ly down_ the stream; Where the grace-ful white swan goes_

cour-ag-ing word, And the skies are not cloud-y all day.
asked as I gazed If their glo-ry exceeds that of ours.
glid-ing a-long Like a maid in a heav-en-ly dream.

CHORUS

Home, home on the range,— Where the

deer and the an-te-lope play; Where seldom is heard a dis-

cour-ag-ing word, And the skies are not cloud-y all day.—

WHOOPEE-TI-YI-YO!

Adapted by JAMES MOREHEAD   *Cowboy Song*

THE LILT is unmistakably Irish; and "sure" there were plenty of Irish among those who settled the West; but except for the flavor of the tune, here is an American folk song of the first rank. Somehow it has escaped the usual mutilation, and nearly all versions are the same, except for an occasional elaboration at the start of the chorus. No other Western folk song presents a more vivid picture of life on the open range.

1. As   I   was a   walk-ing   one morn-ing for pleas-ure I___ spied a cow-punch-er come rid-ing a-long; His hat was throwed back and his spurs___ was a jin-gle, And
2. Ear-ly in spring___ we round up the do-gies,___ Mark 'em and brand 'em and cut off their tails; Then___ we load up the old___ chuck wag-on,
3. Your moth-er was raised 'way down yon-der in Tex-as Where the jim-son weed and the sand-spurs grow; But we're gon-na feed you on prick-ly pears and chol-la,★ Till you're

★ Pronounced 'Choy-a'

148

as he ap-proached he was sing - ing this song:
Hitch up our hors - es and start up the trail,
read - y to hit out for old I - da - ho,

CHORUS

Whoo - pee, ti - yi - yo, Git a - long, lit - tle dog - ies, It's

your mis - for - tune, And none of my own; Whoo - pee

ti - yi - yo, Git a - long, lit - tle dog - ies, For you

know Wy - o - ming will be your new home!

149

O BURY ME NOT ON THE LONE PRAIRIE

Cowboy Song

THIS POIGNANT appeal is also known as *The Dying Cowboy*. Other melodies are used, including some of Indian origin, and the standard tune, here given, occasionally appears with other words, as in the song *Ol' Texas*. Every cowhand knows and understands this song, which is the essence of true poetry.

1. "O bu - ry me not —— on the lone prai - rie!"
2. "O bu - ry me not —— on the lone prai - rie! ——
3. "It mat - ters not, —— so —— I've been told, ——

— These —— words came low ——
— Where —— coy - otes howl ——
— Where the bod - y lies ——

and mournfully From the pallid
and the wind blows free, In a narrow
when the heart grows cold, Yet grant, O

lips of a youth who lay
grave just six by three
grant this wish to me,

On his dying bed
O bury me not
O bury me not

at the close of day.
on the lone prairie!"
on the lone prairie!"

THE OLD CHISHOLM TRAIL

Cowboy Song

IF EVER a song could properly be called a cowboy song it is this one. It literally smells of saddle leather and the trail. Jesse Chisholm was a real man, an Indian trader and interpreter, who (in 1866, according to the Columbia Encyclopedia) found a route over which to drive Texas longhorns from San Antonio and the South to the nearest railroad at Abilene, Kansas, a distance of 800 miles. Back in the 1870s they still called it "Jesse Chisholm's Trail."

1. Well-a come a-long boys and lis-ten to my tale,— I'll tell you of my trou-bles on the
2. I— start-ed up the trail Oc - to-ber twenty - third,— I start-ed up the trail— with the
3. I— went— to the boss— to— draw— my— roll,— And he had— me— fig-ured nine—
4. It's— cloud-y in the west— and it looks— like— rain,— And my derned— old— slick-er's in the
5. On a ten— dol-lar horse—and a for - ty dol-lar sad - dle, I'll— nev - er punch— no— more—
6. Well, I think— I'll— mar-ry me a pret - ty young— squaw,— And— set - tle on the banks— of the

152

RED RIVER VALLEY

Cowboy Song

THIS IS A SONG that "went West" in the 1890s, when that was the thing to do. It went along with the young men who were going that way, and who were leaving sweethearts behind, as they are wont to do. It was then *In the Bright Mohawk Valley,* a New York State popular song by James Kerrigan, but it donned cowboy garb and emerged with a new set of words. Folk singers of the past fifty years have rubbed away the more pretentious form of the original song, and it now has simplicity and sweetness that goes right to the heart.

1. From this val - ley they say you are
2. I have prom - ised you, dar - ling, that
3. As you go to your home by the

Refrain: Come and sit by my side if you

go - ing; I will miss your bright eyes and sweet
nev - er Shall the words from my lips cause you
o - cean, May you nev - er for - get those sweet

love me, Do not has - ten to bid me a -

smile,__ For they say you are tak-ing the
pain,__ And I swear I will love you for-
hours__ That we spent in the Red Riv-er
dieu,__ But re - mem-ber the Red Riv-er

sun - shine____ That____
ev - er____ If you
Val - ley,____ And the
Val - ley,____ And the

bright-ened our path - way a - while.
on - ly will love me a - gain.
love we ex - changed 'mid the flowers.
cow - boy who loved you so true.

D. S. 𝄋

ACROSS THE WIDE MISSOURI
(Shenandoah)

ANONYMOUS

ALWAYS considered a sea chantey—and indeed it is generally sung by sailors—this song undoubtedly had an inland origin. Shenandoah was an Indian chief, according to the song, but the "wide Missouri" is far from the Shenandoah Valley of Virginia. Also, who ever heard of a chantey sung to such a slow tempo? Where is its "lively rhythm," to which the sailors can haul on the halyards? No one can satisfactorily explain these shortcomings of *Shenandoah* (usually pronounced "Shenandore"), but the song seems to have flourished just the same. When the words and music go together so beautifully, what difference does it make?

1. Oh, Shen - an - doah, I long to
2. Oh, Shen - an - doah, I love your
3. Oh, Shen - an - doah, I'm bound to

hear you,)
daugh - ter,} Way— hay, you roll - ing
leave you,)

Oh, Shen - an-doah, I long to
Oh, Shen - an-doah, I love your
Oh, Shen - an-doah, I'll not de -

riv - er!

hear you,
daugh - ter,   Way   hay, we're bound a -
ceive you,

way,   'Cross the wide Mis - sou - ri!

BARB'RY ALLEN

Adapted by JAMES MOREHEAD

Elizabethan Folk Song
Appalachian Mountain Version

THIS IS ONE of the oldest and best-known folk songs of the English-speaking world. There are versions galore of the Scottish tune, hundreds of them in the Southern states alone. The version here given is from the Appalachian Mountains of eastern Tennessee. Note the use of the ancient Gaelic (pentatonic) scale.

1. 'Twas_ in the mer - ry
2. He_ sent his ser - vant
3. She was slow - ly, slow - ly,
4. He_ turned his face un -

month of May, When_ green buds they were
to the town, To the place where she was
get - ting up, And_ slow - ly, slow - ly,
to the wall, And_ death was in him

swell - ing;_ Sweet_ Wil-liam on his
dwell - ing;_ "My_ mas-ter has a
go - ing;_ And the on - ly words she
well - ing;_ "A - dieu, a - dieu, to

death bed lay For love of Barb-'ry Al-len.
call for you, If your name be Barb-'ry Al-len."
said to him Were "Young man, I think you're dy-ing!"
my friends all; Be kind to Barb-'ry Al-len!"

5. When she got in two miles of town
She heard the death-bells ringing.
They rang so clear as if to say:
"Hard-hearted Barb'ry Allen!"

6. "Oh, mother, mother, come make my bed,
"And make it both soft and narrow;
"For Sweet William died for love,
"And I will die for sorrow!"

7. "Oh, father, father, come dig my grave,
"And dig it both deep and narrow;
"For Sweet William died today,
"And I will die tomorrow!"

8. Barb'ry Allen was buried in the old Church tomb,
Sweet William was buried beside her;
Out of William's heart a red rose grew,
Out of Barb'ry Allen's a briar.

9. They grew and grew to the old Church tomb,
Till they could grow no higher;
At the end they tied a true-lover's knot,
And the rose wrapped 'round the briar.

THE BLUE-TAIL FLY

ANONYMOUS

A POPULAR minstrel song of the 1840s. Dan Emmett, who wrote *Dixie,* adapted it and published a version under his name, but the tune is older, and a true folk song. In his Pulitzer Prize poem *John Brown's Body,* Stephen Vincent Benét recognizes it as a popular song of Union soldiers in the Civil War. Burl Ives restored *The Blue-Tail Fly* to popularity in recent times.

1. When I was young I used to wait On master and hand him his plate, And pass the bot-tle when
2. And when he rides in the af-ter-noon, I'd fol-low with a hick-'ry broom; The po - ny, he___ was
3. One day he ride a - round the farm, The flies so num-'rous they did swarm. One chanced to bite him
4. The po - ny run, he___ jump, he pitch, And threw old mas-ter in the ditch. He died and the ju - ry
5. They laid him un - der a 'sim - mon tree; His ep - i - taph is there to see: "Be - neath this stone I'm

he got dry, And brush a-way the blue-tail fly.
like to shy When bit-ten by a blue-tail fly.
on the thigh: The dev-il take the blue-tail fly!
won-dered why: The ver-dict was "the blue-tail fly."
forced to lie, A vic-tim of the blue-tail fly.

CHORUS

Jim-mie crack corn and I don't care,

Jim-mie crack corn and I don't care, Jim-mie crack corn and

I don't care, Old mas-ter's gone a - way!

DOWN IN THE VALLEY

Cowboy Song

BIRMINGHAM JAIL is the name by which it is known throughout the South and Southwest, but many versions have been altered to fit the region, and often a local jail is substituted. The first two stanzas are seldom altered. Most printed versions give the second line of the first stanza as:

"Hang your head over
Hear the wind blow"

—but the editors have never heard the line in actual use.

1. Down in the val - ley,
2. Ros - es love sun - shine,
3. Write me a let - ter,

val - ley so low, ____
vi - 'lets love dew, ____
send it by mail, ____

Late in the eve - ning hear that train
An - gels in heav - en know I love
Send it in care of Bir-ming-ham

162

blow.___ Hear that train blow-
you.___ Know I love you
jail.___ Bir-ming-ham you jail

ing, hear that train blow,___
dear, know I love you,___
house, Bir-ming-ham jail,___

Late in the eve - ning,
An - gels in heav - en
Send it in care of

hear that train blow.___
know I love you.___
Bir - ming - ham jail.___

163

THE FOGGY, FOGGY DEW

ANONYMOUS

ACCORDING TO Carl Sandburg, this song is a condensed novel of real life. He cites as endorsers to this view Sinclair Lewis, Sherwood Anderson, and D. W. Griffith. Griffith (according to Sandburg) once wired from New York to a friend in Chicago: "Send verses Foggy Dew stop tune haunts me..."

1. When I was a bach-'lor, I lived all a-lone, I worked at the weav-er's trade; And the on-ly, on-ly thing I did that was wrong was to

2. One night she knelt close by my side, When I was fast a-sleep, She threw her arms a-round my neck, And

3. Oh, I am a bach-'lor, I live with my son; We work at the weav-er's trade; And ev'-ry sin-gle time I look in-to his eyes He re-

woo— a— fair young maid. I wooed her in the
then— be-gan to weep. She wept, she cried, she
minds me of the fair young maid. He re-minds me of the

win-ter-time And in the sum-mer too;— And the
tore her hair, Ah me, what could I do?— So—
win-ter-time And of the sum-mer too;— And the

on-ly, on-ly thing I did— that was wrong Was to
all night— long I held her in my arms Just to
man-y, man-y times I held her in my arms Just to

keep her from the fog-gy, fog-gy dew.

TURKEY IN THE STRAW

Adapted by JAMES MOREHEAD   ANONYMOUS

THIS SONG is as American as Thankgiving turkey, though its ancestry
may be vaguely Irish. There must be a thousand verses, and at least
six complete titles are on record. Notably, *Old Zip Coon* has the same
tune. It is a square-dance tune that can be counted upon to furnish
a climax, and several hifalutin arrangements have thrust it into the
concert halls. Lists of favorite American tunes invariably include
TURKEY IN THE STRAW.

Well, I had an old hen and she
Well, I hitched up the wa-gon and I
Well, if frogs had wings and

had a wood-en leg, Just the best old hen that
drove down the road, With a two horse wa-gon and a
snakes had hair And au-to-mo-biles went a-

ev - er laid an egg; Well, she
four horse load; Well, I
fly - ing thro' the air; Well, if

laid more eggs than an - y hen on the farm, But an-
cracked my whip and the lead horse sprung, And I
wa-ter-mel-ons grew on a huckle-ber - ry vine,

oth - er lit - tle drink___ wouldn't___ do her an - y harm.
said___ "Good - bye"___ to the wag - on___ tongue.
We'd___ have___ win - ter in the sum - mer___ time.

CHORUS
Tur - key in the hay, in the hay, hay, hay!

Tur - key in the straw, in the straw, straw, straw!

Pick 'em up, shake 'em up, an - y way at all, And___

hit up a tune called___ 'Tur - key in the straw.'

BUFFALO GALS

ANONYMOUS

THE FIRST published copy was by Cool White, a minstrel man, in 1844. It began, "Lubly Fan, woncha come out tonight?" From then on, as the song went on tour, the title was always changed to fit the locale, becoming "Jimtown Gals," "New York Gals," etc. BUFFALO GALS sounds best of all; and the public with unerring finality, determined the title. As *Dance With A Dolly*, with a partly new lyric, the song was a "hit" in 1944.

CHORUS

danced with the gal with the hole in her stock-in' And her

heel kep' a-rock-in' and her toe kep' a-knock-in', I

danced with the gal with the hole in her stock-in'; And we

danced by the light of the moon.

169

HAND ME DOWN MY WALKING CANE

Adapted by JAMES MOREHEAD   AUTHOR UNKNOWN

THOUGH THIS SONG is quite as well known as the great majority of folk songs in the United States, it has avoided appearing in print, and is not included in any of dozens of popular collections. We present a version from the Southern states.

F7   Bb

Hand   me   down___ my___   walk - ing
I   got   drunk___ and I got___   in
The beans was tough___ and the meat___ was
Come here ba - by and___ go___   my
If   I   had listened___what___ ma - ma had

Bbm6

cane___   I'm___   go - ing   a -
jail___   and there was - n't   no -
fat___   and___   oh,   my
bail___   and___   get___   me
said___   I'd be sleep - ing

F

way___   on the mid - night train;
bod - y   for to go___ my   bail,
Lord___ I___ could - n't eat that,
out of this___ bug - gy old jail;
now___ on a feath - er bed,

CHORUS   C7   F

And all my sins are tak-en a - way, Tak-en a - way!___

171

JOHN HENRY

Adapted by JAMES MOREHEAD   *Work Song, Southern U.S.A.*

THROUGHOUT the South there are tall tales about big John Henry. Of the countless versions, all tell essentially the same story: John Henry races against a steam drill, "beats it down," and dies in the effort. The version here given is strictly a "steel-driving" rhythm, accented by the ring of the sledge on the drill.

1. John Hen - ry said__ to his
2. John Hen - ry said__ to his
3. John Hen - ry drove__ in the
4. Laid old John Hen - ry on the

Cap - tain:_____ "Cap-tain, when you
Cap - tain:_____ Says "A man ain't
moun - tain,_____ Drove__ till his
cool-ing board,_____ Looked__ at him
(M - m - m)

go__ to__ town,_____ Bring me back a
noth-in' but a man!_____ 'Fore I let that
ham-mer caught on fire;_____ Ver - y last__
good__ and__ long;_____ Ver - y last__

ON TOP OF OLD SMOKY

ANONYMOUS

"THE LITTLE MOHEE" is sung to the same tune, which comes from the Kentucky Mountains. In 1951 OLD SMOKY suddenly became a "hit" song, reaching No. 1 in popularity in the United States, and sold more than a million phonograph records and nearly as many copies of sheet music. OLD SMOKY could be any high mountain in the 48 states, for the song was first popular when wagon-trains labored across roadless wilderness. The song itself got to Kentucky from England.

1. On— top of Old Smok-y,—— All cover'd with
2. A - court-in's a pleas-ure,—— But part-ing is
3. For a thief, he will rob you,—— And take what you
4. She'll hug you and kiss you——— And tell you more
5. On— top of Old Smok-y,—— All cover'd with

174

snow, _____ I lost my true
grief, _____ And a false heart-ed
have, _____ But a false heart-ed
lies _____ Than the cross ties on the
snow, _____ I lost my true

lov - er, _____ Come a -
lov - er _____ Is ____
lov - er _____ Will __
rail - road, _____ Or the
lov - er, _____ Come a -

court - in' too slow. _____
worse_ than a thief. _____
send you to your grave. _____
stars_ in the skies. _____
court - in' too slow. _____

SHE'LL BE COMIN' 'ROUND THE MOUNTAIN

ANONYMOUS

THIS "RAILROADIN'" song of the 1890s was made from an old spiritual, *When the Chariot Comes*. Grading the roadbeds through the mountains, winding around and tunneling through the irregular terrain, the track gangs could sometimes see the awaited supply train "comin' 'round the mountain," almost half a day away.

1. She'll be comin' 'round the mountain when she comes, (when she comes,) She'll be comin' 'round the mountain when she comes, (when she
2. She'll be drivin' six white horses when she comes, (when she comes,) She'll be drivin' six white horses when she comes, (when she
3. Oh, we'll all go down to meet her when she comes, (when she comes,) Oh, we'll all go down to meet her when she comes, (when she
4. We'll be singin' "Hal-le-lu-jah" when she comes, (when she comes,) We'll be singin' "Hal-le-lu-jah" when she comes, (when she

176

comes,) She'll be com - in' 'round the
comes,) She'll be driv - in' six white
comes,) Oh, we'll all go down to
comes,) We'll be sing - in' "Hal - le -

moun-tain, She'll be com-in' 'round the moun-tain, She'll be
hors - es, She'll be driv-in' six white hors-es, She'll be
meet her, Oh, we'll all go down to meet her, Oh, we'll
lu-jah," We'll be sing-in' "Hal - le - lu-jah," We'll be

com-in' 'round the moun-tain when she comes.__
driv-in' six white hors - es when she comes.__
all go down to meet her when she comes.__
sing-in' "Hal - le - lu-jah" when she comes.__

I GAVE MY LOVE A CHERRY
(The Riddle)

ANONYMOUS

A TENDER Elizabethan song from the Kentucky mountains. Many of the songs sung by the people of this inaccessible area have been preserved almost intact for three hundred and more years, never written down but passed along from generation to generation. Often, the words have no modern meaning but are sung as they were in England during the 16th century.

1. I gave my love a cher-ry that has no stone, I gave my love a chick-en that
2. How can there be a cher-ry that has no stone? How can there be a chick-en that
3. A cher-ry, when it's bloom-ing, it has no stone, A chick-en, when it's pip-ping, it

has   no   bone,   I
has   no   bone?   How
has   no   bone,   A

gave my love a   ring_ that has no end,_ I
can there be a   ring_ that has no end?_How
ring,_ when its roll-ing, it has no end,_ A

gave my love a ba - by with no cry-en.
can there be a ba - by with no cry-en?
ba - by, when it's sleep - ing, has no cry-en.

179

KENTUCKY BABE

RICHARD HENRY BUCK   ADAM GEIBEL

HERE IS a true quartet classic, of which glee clubs and their aud-
iences never tire. Its pianissimo ending is like an art song, and
it is full of opportunities for nuance and effect. Adam Geibel, who
wrote the melody in 1886, was blind from the age of nine days, but
became a Doctor of Music and had his own publishing house. Buck
also wrote the words of *Dear Old Girl*, another quartet favorite.

'Skeet-ers are a-hum-min' on the hon-ey-suck-le vine,

Sleep, Ken-tuck-y Babe; Sand-man is a-com-in' to this

lit-tle one of mine, Sleep Ken-tuck-y Babe!

Sil-v'ry moon is shin-in' in the heav-ens up a-bove,

THERE IS A TAVERN IN THE TOWN

Attributed to
WILLIAM H. HILLS

IN 1883 William H. Hills included this in a collection of college songs, and claimed copyright, but did not enter his name as author, composer, or arranger. The song is probably much older, and English in origin. It was revived in 1934 by Rudy Vallee, a popular singer and orchestra leader.

182

let the part-ing grieve thee, and re-mem-ber that the best of friends must

part, (must part,) A-dieu, a-dieu, kind friends, a-dieu, (yes, a-dieu) I

can no lon-ger stay with you, (stay with you) I'll

hang my harp on a weep-ing wil-low tree, And

may the world go well with thee. (well with thee.)

I'VE BEEN WORKIN' ON THE RAILROAD

ANONYMOUS

No ONE KNOWS the origin of this classic American work-song. The original version, known as *The Levee Sons*, changed to railroad vernacular in the 1890s. The verse is usually omitted, and there is a segue to "Dinah, won't you blow your horn?" further followed by "Someone's in the kitchen with Dinah." *The Eyes of Texas Are Upon You* is set to this tune.

1. Oh, I was born in Mo - bile town, I'm work - in' on the lev - ee. All day I roll the cot - ton down, A - work - in' on the lev - ee.

2. I used to have a dog named Bill, A - work - in' on the lev - ee. He run a - way, but I'm here still, A - work - in' on the lev - ee.

3. That li'l ol' dog set up and beg, A - work - in' on the lev - ee. Till I give him a chick - en leg, A - work - in' on the lev - ee.

OH! SUSANNA

STEPHEN C. FOSTER

WHEN OH! SUSANNA was written, in 1848, Foster literally gave it away, not realizing its value; but its enormous success turned him to songwriting as a profession. Representative of this period in his career, he was slightly imitative, rather than original, following the styles of Dan Emmett and others. There is no doubt, however, that he improved such traditional material as came his way, as witness the lasting power of his songs. OH! SUSANNA is inextricably associated with the banjo, for which it is ideally suited.

1. I come from A - la - ba - ma With my ban-jo on my knee, I'm goin' to Lou-'si - a - na, My true love for to see;— It rained all day the

2. I had a dream the oth - er night, When all was dark and still, I thought I saw Su-san-na A - com-in' down the hill.— A buck-wheat cake was

night I left, The weather it was dry, The sun so hot I
in her hand, A tear was in her eye, Says I, "I'm com-in'

froze to death, Su - san - na don't you cry.
from the south, Su - san - na don't you cry!"

CHORUS

Oh! Su - san - na, Oh, don't you cry for me, I

come from A - la - ba - ma, With my ban-jo on my knee.

AUNT DINAH'S QUILTING PARTY
(When I Saw Sweet Nellie Home)

FRANCIS KYLE   JAMES FLETCHER

THIS SONG is known by many titles, including *The Quilting Party*, *I Was Seeing Nellie Home*, and the ones presented above, of which AUNT DINAH'S QUILTING PARTY is most commonly used; but WHEN I SAW SWEET NELLIE HOME is the real title, as first published in 1867. The harmonies seem made-to-order for barber-shop quartets, college boys favor it as well, and it is much parodied. Sigmund Spaeth points to the use of its melody in Cole Porter's *Old Fashioned Garden*, and the novelty song of 1923, *Yes! We Have No Bananas*.

1. In the sky the bright stars
2. On my arm a soft hand
3. On my lips a whis - per
4. On my life new hopes were

glit - tered,— On the bank the pale moon
rest - ed,— Rest - ed light as o - cean
trem - bled,— Trem - bled till it dared to
dawn - ing,— And those hopes have liv'd and

shone;)
foam;)
come;)   And 'twas from Aunt Di - nah's
grown;)

quilt-ing par-ty, I was see-ing Nel-lie home.

CHORUS

I was see-ing Nel-lie home, — I was

see-ing Nel-lie home; And 'twas from Aunt Di-nah's

quilt-ing par-ty, I was see-ing Nel-lie home.

COCKLES AND MUSSELS
(Molly Malone)

Adapted and arranged by
JAMES MOREHEAD

ANONYMOUS

COCKLES AND MUSSELS, an Irish folk song also known as MOLLY MALONE, has been a "hit" several times, most recently because of its use in the motion picture *A Tree Grows in Brooklyn*. "Wheelbarrow," as used in the song, means a small cart.

1. In Dub-lin's fair cit-y, where girls are so pret-ty, 'Twas there that I first met sweet Mol-ly Ma-lone, As she wheel'd her wheel-

2. She was a fish-mon-ger, and sure 'twas no won-der, Her fa-ther and moth-er were fish-mon-gers too; And they each wheel'd a

3. She died of a fe-ver, and no one could save her, And that's all I know of sweet Mol-ly Ma-lone; Now her ghost wheels her

bar-row through streets broad and nar-row,
bar-row through streets broad and nar-row, } Crying,
bar-row through streets broad and nar-row,

"Cock-les and Mus-sels! a - live, a-live - oh!"

CHORUS

"A - live, a-live - oh! — A - live, a-live - oh!" Cry-ing,

"Cock-les, and Mus-sels, a - live, — a-live - oh!"

COMIN' THROUGH THE RYE

Attributed to
ROBERT BURNS

Traditional

THE QUESTION IS, did Burns write the words? Or did he merely improve upon already existing lines, as he often did? In a collection of Scottish songs edited by Angus MacKay, about 1858, the song is listed as anonymous, with the suggestion that Burns altered the verses. As early as 1784 the tune appeared as *The Miller's Daughter*, a *strathspey* (Scottish dance) full of the "Scotch snap," or accented sixteenth note followed by a dotted eighth. In America, the first publication was about 1828.

1. If a bod-y meet a bod-y
2. If a bod-y meet a bod-y
3. A-mang the train there is a swain I

Com-in' thro' the rye,
Com-in' frae the town,
dear-ly love my-sel'; But

If a bod-y kiss a bod-y,
If a bod-y greet a bod-y,
what's his name, or where's his hame, I

Need a bod - y cry?
Need a bod - y frown?
Ev-'ry las-sie din - na choose to tell.

has her lad - die, Nane, they say, ha'e I;

Yet a' the lads they

smile on me, When com - in' thro' the rye.

193

THE CAMPBELLS ARE COMIN'

ANONYMOUS

THE SONG refers to the Campbell clan of Scotland, whose chieftains were the Earls, and later Dukes, of Argyll. It is martial music. The claymore of the second stanza is a two-handed sword, hung at the warrior's side; the pibroch of the third stanza is a warlike air played by the pipes for a marching army. Today a playing of THE CAMPBELLS ARE COMIN' summons up a picture of kilts and bonnets and other American imagery regarding the highland Scots.

The Camp-bells are com-in', O - ho! O - ho! The

Camp-bells are com - in', O - ho! O - ho! The

Camp-bells are com - in' From bon-nie Loch Lo-mond, The

194

Camp-bells are com - in', O - ho! O - ho!

1. The great Ar - gyle, he goes be - fore, He
2. With bon - net blue, auld Scot-ties pride, And
3. Hark! hark! the Pib - roch's sound I hear, Now

makes the guns and can-nons roar; With sound of trum-pet,
broad clay-more hung at their side, With plumes all nodding
bon-nie las - sie, din - na fear; 'Tis hon - or calls, I

pipe and drum, And ban - ners wav-ing in the sun.
in the wind, They have not left a man be-hind.
must a - way, Ar - gyle's the word and ours the day.

THE CAMPTOWN RACES

STEPHEN C. FOSTER

SCHOLARS have found that this song of Foster's is not entirely original; that it resembles a folk song called *Hoodah Day*, the chantey *Sacramento*, and the spiritual *Roll, Jordan, Roll*. The resemblance consists mostly of a simple major chord, 1-3-5-8. Foster wrote the words, which is more important, and probably used a standard folk tune of his time. The song was published in 1850, the year of Foster's marriage. Sigmund Spaeth says: ".... if Stephen Foster could invent *O Susanna*, he could just as easily create *Camptown Races*."

1. The Camptown la - dies sing this song: Doo-dah!
2. The long-tail'd fil-ly and the big black 'hoss, 'Doodah!
3. Oh, see them fly-in' on a ten mile heat, Doodah!

doo-dah! The Camptown race track nine miles long,
doo-dah! They fly the track and they both cut 'cross,
doo-dah! Round the race track, then re - peat,

Oh! doo-dah day! I came down here with a
Oh! doo-dah day! The blind 'hoss' stick in a
Oh! doo-dah day! I keep my mon-ey in an

pock-et full of tin, Doo-dah! doo-dah! I'm
big_ mud hole, Doo-dah! doo-dah! Can't
old_ tow bag, Doo-dah! doo-dah! I'll

go-in' back home with my hat caved in, Oh, doo-dah day!
touch the bot-tom with a ten foot pole Oh, doo-dah day!
bet my mon-ey on the bob-tail nag, Oh, doo-dah day!

CHORUS

Goin' to run all night, Goin' to run all day, I'll_

bet my money on the bob-tail nag, Somebody bet on the bay.

197

TAKE ME OUT TO THE BALL GAME

Jack Norworth   Albert von Tilzer

This is the official song of America's traditional national game, but the writers of it were not necessarily baseball fans when the song was published in 1908; that was an era when popular songs had topical themes. The original lyric had a "verse" in which Nelly Kelly begged her escort to take her out to the ball game. Albert was youngest of the famous Von Tilzer brothers, who made history in popular American music; Jack Norworth, a skilled songwriter, was husband of Nora Bayes and may have done more than merely collaborate in her biggest song, *Shine On, Harvest Moon*.

Take me out to the ball - game,

Take me out to the park ____ Buy me some

pea-nuts and crack - er - jack I don't care if I

nev - er come back, Let me root root root for the home team, If they don't win it's a shame.___ For it's one, two, three strikes, "You're out!" at the old ball - game.___

SCHOOL DAYS

WILL D. COBB   GUS EDWARDS

THE FAMILIAR AND SUCCESSFUL SONGS he wrote are numerous, yet this simple and homely one is the classic contribution of Gus Edwards. Born in Germany in 1879, named Gustav Edward Simon, and brought to the United States as a child, he became a successful songwriter, publisher, vaudevillian and show producer in his early twenties. He wrote SCHOOL DAYS (1907) for a vaudeville act in which he introduced as children such later stars as Eddie Cantor, George Jessel, Groucho Marx, and many others. Cobb, a successful lyricist of those times, wrote several big songs with Edwards.

School days, school days, dear old Gold-en Rule days, Read-ing and writ-ing and 'rith-ma-tic, Taught to the tune of a

200

hick - 'ry stick, You were my queen in cal - i -

co, I was your bash - ful bare - foot

beau, And you wrote on my slate "I love you,

Joe," When we were a cou - ple of kids. __

CASEY JONES

T. LAWRENCE SEIBERT

EDDIE NEWTON

There is no more American song. From our history in which railroads made America's greatness, this is the No. 1 railroad song. It is typical of the topical ballads that flourished before it was published (1909). There are forty-five versions and the Seibert-Newton one is not necessarily the first, but who knows? The incident is actual; John Luther Jones, called Casey because he came from Cayce, Kentucky, died as recounted in the ballad, taking a train called the Cannonball out of Memphis.

1. Come all you round-ers, if you want to hear a story about a brave en-gi-neer, Ca-sey Jones was the round-er's name, On a six eight wheel-er boys, he won his fame. The

2. Put in your wa-ter and sho-vel your coal, Put your head out the win-dow watch them driv-ers roll, I'll run her till she leaves the rail, 'Cause I'm eight hours late with the West-ern mail." He

3. Ca-sey pulled up that Re-no hill He toot-ed for the cross-ing with an aw-ful shrill, The switch-man knew by the en-gine's moan That the man at the throttle was Ca-sey Jones. He

4. Ca-sey said just be-fore he died "There's two more roads that I'd like to ride, The fire-man said "What could that be?" "The South-ern Pa-ci-fic and the San-ta Fe." Mrs.

202

call-er called Ca-sey at a half past four, He
looked at his watch and his watch was slow, He
pulled up with-in two miles of the place, He
Jones sat on her bed a - sigh'n, Just re-

kissed his wife at the sta - tion door, He
looked at the wa-ter and the wa-ter was low, He
num-ber four stared him right in the face, He
ceived a mes - sage that Ca-sey was dy-ing, Said

mount-ed to the ca-bin with his or-ders in his hand, And he
turned to the fire - man and he said, "Boy, we're
turned to the fire-man said "Boy, you bet-ter jump, Cause there's
"Go to bed, chil - dren, hush your cry - in', Cause you

took his fare-well trip to the Prom-ised Land.
goin' to reach Fris - co but we'll all be dead."
two lo-co-mo-tives that's a goin' to bump."
got an-oth-er pa-pa on the Salt Lake Line."

CHORUS

Ca-sey Jones,__ mount-ed to the ca-bin (Well__)
Ca-sey Jones,__ goin' to reach Fris-co (Well__)
Ca-sey Jones,__ two__ lo-co-mo-tives (Yes__)
Mrs. Ca-sey Jones,__ got an-oth-er pa-pa, Mrs.

Ca-sey Jones,__ with his or-ders in his hand,
Ca-sey Jones,__ but we'll all__ be__ dead,
Ca-sey Jones,__ that's a-goin' to__ bump,
Ca-sey Jones,__ on the Salt__ Lake__ Line, Mrs.

Ca-sey Jones,__ mount-ed to the cab-in and he
Ca-sey Jones,__ goin' to reach__ Fris-co, we're__
Ca-sey Jones,__ two__ lo-co-mo-tives, There's__
Ca-sey Jones,__ got an-oth-er pa-pa, 'Cause you

took his fare-well trip__ to the Prom-ised__ Land.
goin' to reach Fris-co but we'll all be__ dead."
two__ lo-co-mo-tives that's a goin' to__ bump."
got an-oth-er pa-pa on the Salt Lake__ Line."__

HYMNS

GLORIA PATRI

H. W. GREATOREX

THIS IS ONE of the time-honored forms of doxology, or expression of praise of God. The *Gloria in excelsis* (glory [be to God] in the highest) and *Gloria Patri* (glory [be to] the Father) are accounted somewhat more formal than the Doxology shown on the front endpages of this book. The text of the *Gloria Patri* below is said to derive from St. Thomas Aquinas, can be traced to a Meissen Breviary of the early 16th century, and was rendered by Dr. John Mason Neale in 1851. It is sung in almost all Christian churches.

Glo-ry be to the Fa-ther, and to the Son, and to the ho-ly Ghost; As it was in the be-gin-ning, is now, and ev-er shall be, world with-out end. A - men, A - men.

OUR GOD, OUR HELP IN AGES PAST

Isaac Watts

William Croft

St. Anne's, C.M.

IN A TIME of crisis for the Church of England, Watts based his poem upon the 90th Psalm. The tune is named for the church where Croft was organist. The hymn appears in almost all hymn books (often with the beginning altered to "O God...") and is much used for New Year's Day. At St. Clement's Church in London it is rung daily on the bells.

1. Our God, our help in a-ges past, Our hope for years to come, Our shel-ter from the storm-y blast, And our e-ter-nal home!

2. Un-der the shad-ow of Thy throne Thy saints have dwelt se-cure; Suf-fi-cient is Thine arm a-lone, And our de-fence is sure.

3. Be-fore the hills in or-der stood, Or earth re-ceive her frame, From ev-er-last-ing Thou art God, To end-less years the same.

4. A thou-sand a-ges in Thy sight Are like an eve-ning gone; Short as the watch that ends the night Be-fore the ris-ing sun.

5. Time, like an ev-er roll-ing stream, Bears all its sons a-way; They fly, for-got-ten as a dream Dies at the ope-ning day.

6. Our God, our help in a-ges past, Our hope for years to come, Be Thou our guard while life shall last, And our e-ter-nal home!

HOLY, HOLY, HOLY!

REGINALD HEBER · · · · · · · JOHN BACCHUS DYKES

Nicaea, P.M.

THIS WAS regarded by Tennyson as one of the finest of all hymns and it was sung at his burial in Westminster Abbey. It was adapted by Bishop Heber from the "cadence of the Apocalypse," REVELATION 4:8, "and they rest not day and night, saying Holy, holy, holy, Lord God Almighty, which was, and is, and is to come."

1. Ho-ly, Ho-ly, Ho - ly!— Lord God Al-might-y! Ear - ly in the morn-ing our song shall rise to Thee;
2. Ho-ly, Ho-ly, Ho - ly!— all the saints a-dore Thee, Cast-ing down their gold-en crowns a - round the glass-y sea;
3. Ho-ly, Ho-ly, Ho - ly!— tho' the dark-ness hide Thee, Though the eye of sin-ful man Thy glo - ry may not see,

Ho - ly, Ho - ly, Ho - ly!
Cher - u - bim and ser - aphim
On - ly Thou art Ho - ly;

Mer - ci - ful and might - y!
fall - ing down be - fore Thee,
there is none be - side Thee,

God in three Per - sons,
Which wert and art, and
Per - fect in pow'r, in

bless - ed Trin - i - ty!
ev - er - more shall be.
love, and pur - i - ty.

209

A MIGHTY FORTRESS

Translated by
FREDERICK H. HEDGE

MARTIN LUTHER

Ein Feste Burg,
8.7.8.7.6.6.6.7.

KNOWN AS "the battle hymn of the reformation," this is a truly historic hymn. Meyerbeer incorporated it into his opera *Les Huguenots*, Wagner into *Der Kaisermarsch*, Mendelssohn in his *Reformation Symphony*. The famous chorale was sung in Boston in 1869 by a chorus of ten thousand voices, accompanied by a thousand-piece orchestra directed by Patrick S. Gilmore.

1. A might-y Fort-ress is our God, A
2. Did we in our own strength confide, Our
3. And tho'this world, with dev - ils filled, Should

Bul-wark nev - er fail - ing; Our Help-er He a-
striv-ing would be los - ing; Were not the right man
threat-en to un-do_ us; We will not fear for

mid the flood Of mor-tal ills pre - vail - ing.
on our side, The man of God's own choos - ing.
God hath will'd His truth to tri-umph through us.

For still our an - cient foe Doth
Doth ask who that may be? Christ
Let goods and kin - dred go, This

seek to work his woe: His craft and pow'r are
Je - sus it is He! Lord Sab - a - oth His
mor-tal life al - so; The bod-y they may

great, And armed with cru - el hate, On
name, From age to age the same; And
kill; God's truth a - bid-eth still, His

earth is not His e - qual.
He must win the bat - tle.
king-dom is for - ev - er.

THE CHURCH'S ONE FOUNDATION

SAMUEL J. STONE   SAMUEL S. WESLEY

Aurelia, 7s, 6s, D.

WRITTEN in 1866 during the "Colenso Controversy" in the Church of England, when the authenticity of the Pentateuch was questioned, this hymn is one of twelve based upon the articles of the Apostles' Creed. The Reverend Dr. Stone, who was then curate of Windsor, figured prominently in the controversy. The tune had previously been used for *Jerusalem the Golden*, from which it derives its name *Aurelia* (golden).

1. The Church's one foun-da-tion Is Je-sus Christ her Lord; She is His new cre-a-tion By wa-ter and the word. From

2. Though with a scorn-ful won-der, Men see her sore op-prest, By schi-sms rent a-sun-der, By her-e-sies dis-trest; Yet

3. 'Mid toil and trib-u-la-tion, And tu-mult of her war, She waits the con-sum-ma-tion Of peace for-ev-er-more; Till

heav'n He came and sought her To
saints their watch are keep-ing, Their
with the vi - sion glo-rious Her

be His ho - ly Bride; With
cry goes up "How long?" And
long - ing eyes are blest, And

His own blood He bought Her, And
soon the night of weep-ing Shall
the great Church vic - to - rious, Shall

for Her life He died.
be the morn of song.
be the Church of rest.

ANCIENT OF DAYS

William Croswell Doane   J. Albert Jeffrey
Albany, 11.10.11.10

Written in 1886 for the bicentenary in celebration of the chartering of the city of Albany, New York. The title is derived from Daniel 7:9, "I beheld till the thrones were cast down, and the Ancient of days did sit."

1. An - cient of days, Who
2. O Ho - ly Fa - ther,
3. O Ho - ly Je - sus,
4. O Ho - ly Ghost, the
5. O Tri - une God, with

sit - test throned in glo - ry;
Who hast led Thy chil - dren
Prince of Peace and Sav - iour,
Lord and the Life - Giv - er,
heart and voice a - dor - ing,

To Thee all knees are bent, all voic - es pray;
In all the a - ges, with the fire and cloud,
To Thee we owe the peace that still pre-vails,
Thine is the quick'ning pow'r that gives in-crease.
Praise we the good-ness that has crown'd our day;

214

Thy love has bless'd the
Thro' seas dry - shod; thro'
Still - ing the rude wills
From Thee have flowed, as
Pray we, that Thou wilt

wide world's won - drous sto - ry,
wea - 'ry wastes be - wil - d'ring
of men's wild be - hav - iour,
from a pleas - ant riv - er,
hear us, still im - plor - ing

With light and life since E - den's dawn-ing day.
To Thee, in rev - 'rent love, our hearts are bowed.
And calm-ing pas - sion's fierce and storm - y gales.
Our plen - ty, wealth, pros-per - i - ty and peace.
Thy love and fa - vor, kept to us al-way.

ALL PRAISE TO THEE, MY GOD, THIS NIGHT

THOMAS KEN

CHARLES F. GOUNOD

Evening Hymn, L.M.D.

PROBABLY one of the most famous English hymns; note that Stanza 4 is familiar as the *Doxology*. Often sung to Tallis' *Canon*, it dates from 1692. It was Thomas Ken, brother-in-law of Izaak Walton the angler, who refused to accommodate Nell Gwyn when she visited Winchester with Charles II. The King so admired his courage that he appointed him Bishop of Bath and Wells.

1. All praise to Thee, my God this night For all the bless-ings of the light. Keep me, oh, keep me, King of kings, Be-neath Thine own al-might-y wings.

3. Oh, may my soul on Thee re-pose, And may sweet sleep my eye-lids close, Sleep that shall me more vig-'rous make To serve my God when I a-wake!

2. For - give me Lord, for Thy dear Son, The
4. Praise God from whom all bless-ings flow; Praise

ill that I this day have done That
Him all crea-tures here be - low; Praise

with the world, my - self, and Thee I,
Him a - bove, ye heav'n - ly host; Praise

ere I sleep, at peace may be.
Fa - ther, Son, and Ho - ly Ghost.

FAITH OF OUR FATHERS

FREDERICK W. FABER

HENRI F. HEMY
JAMES G. WALTON

St. Catherine, L.M.

FREDERICK FABER was brought up a Calvinist. After he was ordained at Oxford, he came under the influence of John H. Newman and followed him into the Catholic Church. This hymn was written some years later and the original text plainly applied to the Oxford Movement and the Catholic Communion:

Faith of our Fathers! Mary's prayers
Shall win our country back to Thee;
And through the truth that comes from God,
England shall then indeed be free.

1. Faith of our fa - thers, liv - ing
2. Faith of our fa - thers, we will
3. Faith of our fa - thers, we will

still   In spite of dun-geon, fire and
strive   To win all na-tions un - to
love   Both friend and foe in all our

sword,   Oh how our hearts beat
thee;   And through the truth that
strife, And preach thee, too,— as

high_ with joy When - e'er we
comes from God Man - kind shall
love_ knows how By kind - ly

hear that glo - rious word!
then in - deed be free.
words and vir - tuous life.

REFRAIN

Faith of our fa - thers, ho - ly faith,

We will be true to thee till death. A - men.

DEAR LORD AND FATHER OF MANKIND

JOHN GREENLEAF WHITTIER   FREDERICK C. MAKER

Rest (Elton), 8.6.8.8.6.

MEDITATION was a favorite theme to the great poet, and in this hymn he pays tribute to the self-knowledge that is found in solitude. The verses are part of a major poem, *The Brewing of Soma*, wherein Whittier compares our communion of the spirit with the Indian use of the intoxicant "soma," mistakenly believed to have produced rapport with God. The tune was first published in London, in *The Church Hymnary*, in 1887. Frederick Maker used commendable restraint in finding a perfect musical form without resorting to a repetition of the last line of each stanza, which would seem the obvious way out of a difficult pattern.

1. Dear Lord and Fa - ther of man-kind, For - give our fe - v'rish
2. In sim - ple trust like theirs who heard, Be - side the Syr - ian
3. O Sab - bath rest by Gal - i - lee! O calm of hills a -
4. Drop thy still dews of qui - et - ness, Till all our striv - ings
5. Breathe thro' the heats of our de - sire Thy cool - ness and thy

ways! Re - clothe us in our
sea, The gra - cious call - ing
bove, Where Je - sus knelt to
cease; Take from our souls the
balm; Let sense be dumb, let

right - ful mind; In pur - er lives Thy
of the Lord, Let us, like them, with -
share with Thee The si - lence of e -
strain and stress, And let our or - dered
flesh re - tire; Speak through the earth - quake,

serv - ice find, In deep - er rev - 'rence, praise.
out a word, Rise up and fol - low Thee.
ter - ni - ty, In - ter - pret - ed by love!
lives con - fess The beau - ty of Thy peace.
wind, and fire, O still small voice of calm!

NEARER, MY GOD, TO THEE

SARAH (FLOWER) ADAMS   LOWELL MASON

Bethany, 6s, 4s.

MRS. ADAMS was a talented actress, but her health would not permit her to follow that profession. She turned to writing, together with her sister Elizabeth. Tuberculosis struck Elizabeth, and she died in 1846. Sarah, who had contracted the disease while acting as nurse, died two years later. When the great liner *Titanic* went down in 1912, the band played NEARER, MY GOD, TO THEE as the water rose, and 1,500 passengers and crewmen sang the inspiring words as if they too saw the vision of Jacob at Bethel (GENESIS 28:10-22).

1. Near - er, my God, to Thee, near - er, to Thee:
2. Though like the wan - der - er, the sun gone down,
3. There let the way ap - pear steps un - to heav'n;

E'en though it be a cross that raiseth me,
Dark - ness be o - ver me, my rest a stone,
All that Thou send - est me in mer - cy giv'n;

Still all my song shall be,
Yet in my dreams I'd be } Near - er my God, to Thee,
An - gels to beck - on me,

Near - er, my God, to Thee, near - er to Thee.

GIVE TO OUR GOD IMMORTAL PRAISE

ISAAC WATTS   DUKE STREET L.M.   JOHN HATTON

THIS HYMN RANKED FIFTH in popularity among Lutherans (according to a poll taken by *The Lutheran* magazine) in 1965. It was in Sir Isaac Watts' *Psalms of David* in 1719 and it has been set to other tunes—just as the tune below has been used for other hymns, notably *I Know That My Redeemer Lives*. The composer John Hatton died in 1793 and was not the more prolific John Hatton of Liverpool, born 1809; in fact, no connection between them can be proved. But there must have been one, for the earlier John Hatton lived and died near Liverpool in the village of St. Helens and on Duke Street,

1. Give to our God immortal praise,
2. Give to the Lord of lords renown,
3. He sent His Son with power to save
4. Through this vain world He guides our feet

Mercy and truth are all His ways.
The King of kings with glory crown,
From guilt and darkness and the grave.
And leads us to His heav'nly seat.

Wonders of grace to God belong,
His mercies ever shall endure,
Wonders of grace to God belong,
His mercies ever shall endure,

Repeat His mercies in your song.
When lords and kings are known no more,
Repeat His mercies in your song.
When this vain world shall be no more.

COME, THOU ALMIGHTY KING

ANONYMOUS

FELICE GIARDINI

Trinity, 6s, 4s.

THE WORDS are often ascribed to Charles Wesley because they were first printed in a leaflet published by the Wesleys, but there is no evidence that he wrote them and certainly he never claimed them. Also, the meter is one he never used. Probably the poem was written in imitation of *God Save Our Gracious King*, which had been sung to the same tune a few years earlier. In Britain the tune is known as *Moscow* (where Giardini died). It is also known as *Florence*, *Fairford*, and *Giardini*.

1. Come, Thou al - might - y King, Help us Thy name to sing,
2. Come, Thou in - car - nate Word, Gird on Thy might - y sword;
3. Come, ho - ly Com - fort - er! Thy sa - cred wit - ness bear,
4. To the great One in Three, The high - est prais - es be,

Help us to praise:
Our pray'r at - tend:
In this glad hour:
Hence ev - er - more!

Fa - ther! all glo - ri - ous,
Come and Thy peo - ple bless
Thou, who al - might - y art,
His sov - 'reign ma - jes - ty

O'er all vic - to - ri - ous, Come and reign
And give Thy word suc - cess: Spir - it of
Now rule in ev - 'ry heart And ne'er from
May we in Glo - ry see, And to e -

o - ver us, An - cient of Days!
ho - li - ness! On us de - scend.
us de - part, Spir - it of pow'r!
ter - ni - ty Love and a - dore.

GUIDE ME, O THOU GREAT JEHOVAH

WILLIAM WILLIAMS   THOMAS HASTINGS

Zion, 8s, 7s, 4s, 7s.

WILLIAM WILIALMS was born in 1717 on a farm in Pantycelyn, Wales. And, says Albert E. Bailey, the Williams family still lives there. Of the hundreds of hymns that he wrote, only this one is important in today's hymnals. He wrote it originally in Welsh. The first stanza was translated by Peter Williams (not related to W.W.) in 1771. Stanzas 2 and 3 were also translated by him, but John Williams, son of William, retranslated them in 1772. (Some sources say the senior Williams retranslated them himself.) The hymn has been translated into 75 languages.

1. Guide me, O Thou great Je-
2. O - pen now the crys - tal
3. When I tread the verge of

ho - vah, Pil - grim thro' this bar - ren
foun-tain, Whence the heal - ing wa - ters
Jor - dan, Bid my anx - ious fears sub-

land: I am weak, but Thou art
flow; Let the fier - y, cloud - y
side; Bear me through the swel - ling

might - y, Hold me with Thy pow'r - ful
pil - lar Lead me all my jour - ney
cur - rent, Land me safe on Ca - naan's

hand: Bread of heav - en, Feed me
thro': Strong De - liv - 'rer, Be Thou
side: Songs of prais - es I will

till I want no more, Bread of
still my strength and shield, Strong De -
ev - er give to Thee, Songs of

heav - en, Feed me till I want no more.
liv - 'rer, Be Thou still my strength and shield.
prais-es I will ev - er give to Thee.

COME, THOU FOUNT
OF EVERY BLESSING

ROBERT ROBINSON   JOHN WYETH

Nettleton, 8.7.8.7.D.

REPENTANT after a youth misspent in carousing, Robinson became a minister. He was essentially a nonconformist, although at various times he functioned as a member of many denominations. This was the favorite hymn of Mrs. Francis E. Clark, who with her husband founded the Christian Endeavor Society. At her suggestion, an ebenezer, or collective stone monument (1 SAMUEL 7:13), was raised in its honor.

1. Come, Thou Fount of ev-'ry bless-ing, Tune my heart to sing Thy grace; Streams of mer-cy, nev-er
2. Here I raise mine Eb-en-e-zer; Hith-er by Thy help I'm come; And I hope, by Thy good
3. Oh, to grace how great a debt-or Dai-ly I'm con-strained to be! Let Thy good-ness, like a

ceas-ing, Call for songs of loud-est praise.
pleas-ure, Safe-ly to ar-rive at home.
fet-ter, Bind my wan-d'ring heart to Thee:

Teach me some me-lo-dious son-net, Sung by
Je - sus sought me when a stran-ger, Wan-der-ing
Prone to wan-der, Lord, I feel it, Prone to

flam-ing tongues a - bove; Praise the
from the fold of God; He, to
leave the God I love; Here's my

mount I'm fixed up-on it Mount of Thy re-deem-ing love.
res-cue me from danger, Inter-posed His precious blood.
heart, Oh, take and seal it; Seal it for Thy courts a - bove.

ROCK OF AGES

AUGUSTUS M. TOPLADY   THOMAS HASTINGS

Toplady, seven 6s

THE WORD *rock* appears metaphorically throughout the Old and
New Testaments. In 1 CORINTHIANS 10:4, Paul says, "They drank of
that spiritual Rock . . . and that Rock was Christ." Toplady was a
militant opponent of Wesley, at whom he hurled constant insult and
invective. His hymn contains his creed, but today the old feud
is forgotten, and this is one of the most popular hymns in English.
In the original version "wounded side" read "riven side"; and the
last line of the first stanza appears as "Cleanse me from its guilt
and power."

1. Rock of A - ges, cleft for
2. Not the la - bor of my
3. While I draw this fleet - ing

me, Let me hide my - self in
hands Can ful - fil Thy law's de -
breath, While mine eyes shall close in

Thee; Let the wa - ter and the
mands; Could my zeal no res - pite
death, When I soar to worlds un -

blood, From Thy wound - ed side which
know, Could my tears for - ev - er
known, See Thee on Thy judg-ment

flowed, Be of sin the dou - ble
flow, All for sin could not a -
throne, Rock of A - ges cleft for

cure, Save from guilt and make me pure.
tone, Thou must save, and Thou a - lone.
me, Let me hide my-self in Thee.

LEAD, KINDLY LIGHT

John H. Newman

John Bacchus Dykes

Lux Benigna, Irregular

Cardinal Newman credited Dykes' superb tune with the success of his hymn. It became prominent here through having been sung at the funeral of President McKinley, but its use at funerals is probably misinterpretation. Newman had been torn by indecision for many years whether to become a Catholic, which he subsequently did. The words are most probably a prayer for guidance, wherein "light" means a "pillar of fire" such as led the Israelites through the wilderness (Exodus 13:22), and "kindly" has the Elizabethan sense of "inner" or "innate."

1. Lead, kind-ly Light, a-mid th'en-cir-cling gloom,— Lead Thou me— on! The night is dark, and I am far from home;—

2. I was not ev-er thus, nor prayed that Thou — Shouldst lead me— on; I loved to choose and see my path; but now—

3. So long Thy pow'r hath blest me, sure it still— Will lead me— on O'er moor and fen, o'er crag and tor-rent, till—

Lead Thou me on! Keep Thou my feet; I
Lead Thou me on! I loved the gar - ish
The night is gone, And with the morn those

do not ask to see____ The dis - tant
day, and spite of fears,____ Pride ruled my
an - gel fa - ces smile,____ Which I have

scene; one step e - nough for me.____
will. Re - mem - ber not____ past years!
loved long since, and lost____ a - while!

233

SWEET HOUR OF PRAYER

WILLIAM W. WALFORD

WILLIAM B. BRADBURY

Prayer, L.M.D.

THE REVEREND THOMAS SALMON, of Coleshill, England, sailed for New York on a visit, taking with him some verses he had taken in dictation from his blind friend, the Reverend William Walford. He had the verses published in the New York *Observer*. This was in 1845. Fourteen years later the poem came to the attention of the organist and composer William Bradbury, and the hymn was published among his *Cottage Melodies*. When we remember that Walford's life was filled with "seasons of distress and grief" it is good to know that his hymn has brought comfort to so many in like adversity.

1. Sweet hour of pray'r! Sweet hour of pray'r! That calls me from a world of care, And bids me, at my Fa-ther's throne, Make

2. Sweet hour of pray'r! Sweet hour of pray'r! Thy wings shall my pe-ti-tion bear, To Him whose truth and faith-ful-ness En -

3. Sweet hour of pray'r! Sweet hour of pray'r! May I thy con-so-la-tion share; Till from Mount Pis-gah's loft-y height, I

all my wants and wish - es known.
gage the wait - ing soul to bless.
view my home, and take my flight.

In sea - sons of dis-tress and grief, My soul has
And since He bids me seek His face, Be-lieve His
This robe of flesh I'll drop, and rise To seize the

oft - en found re - lief, And oft es - caped the
word and trust His grace, I'll cast on Him my
ev - er-last-ing prize; And shout, while pass - ing

tempt-er's snare, By thy re-turn sweet hour of pray'r.
ev - 'ry care, And wait for thee, sweet hour of pray'r.
thro' the air, Fare-well, fare-well, sweet hour of pray'r.

WHAT SHALL I PRAY FOR TODAY?

ALBERT *and* JAMES MOREHEAD

Tilly Foster, P.M.

HERE is a question with which one may search himself in a materialistic world. Shall we pray, as St. Augustine admits that he did, "God make me pure . . . but not yet"; or, as the Reverend Frank H. Ferris suggests, shall we "run the calculated risks of prayer: of seeing ourselves as we are; of having our prayers answered"? The message here is that one should pray for strength and faith but not for the fulfilment of desire selfishly felt.

1. What shall I pray for to-day?___
2. How shall I pray when I pray,—
3. What shall I say when I pray,—

Pray for a heart that is true;___
Sunk-en in sin and in shame?___
Say to our Fath-er a-bove?___

True to Him Who is free from
Mark His word that your pray'r is
"Lord Di-vine, let the praise be

sin, Who will share your pray'r with you;___
heard, if you ask in Je - sus' name;___
Thine, Who art truth, and hope, and love;___

Pray to be strong in your faith;_ His is the
Fall on your knees when you pray,_ Bow to His
Thine be the glo - ri - ous Name,_ Name re -

grace to for - give,_ Know that He is your
Heav - en - ly might,_ Find sal - va - tion in
vered and a - dored,_ Hear this pray'r, our

Sav - iour, Who died that you might live.___
Je - sus, The Way, the Life, the Light.___
Fath - er, Thru Je - sus Christ, our Lord."

237

WHAT A FRIEND WE HAVE IN JESUS

JOSEPH SCRIVEN   CHARLES C. CONVERSE

Erie, 8.7.8.7.D

THE DAY before Joseph Scriven was to have been married, his young bride-to-be was tragically drowned. He never recovered from the shock. Migrating to America from his native Ireland, he devoted the rest of his life to the poor, doing odd jobs and accepting only enough money for his simple needs. Ira D. Sankey, in *My Life and Sacred Songs*, says that a neighbor discovered the poem while visiting Scriven during his illness, and was told that "The Lord and I did it between us."

1. What a Friend we have in Je - sus,
2. Have we tri - als and temp - ta - tions?
3. Are we weak and heav - y - la - den,

All our sins and griefs to bear!
Is there trou - ble an - y - where?
Cum-bered with a load of care?

What a priv - i - lege to car - ry
We should nev - er be dis - cour - aged,
Pre - cious Sav - ior, still our ref - uge,

Ev - 'ry - thing to God in prayer!
Take it to the Lord in prayer.
Take it to the Lord in prayer.

Oh what peace we oft - en for - feit,
Can we find a friend so faith - ful
Do thy friends de - spise, for - sake thee?

Oh what need-less pain we bear, All be-cause we do not
Who will all our sor-rows share? Je-sus knows our ev'ry
Take it to the Lord in prayer; In His arms He'll take and

car - ry Ev - 'ry-thing to God in prayer!
weak-ness, Take it to the Lord in prayer.
shield thee, Thou wilt find a sol-ace there.

ABIDE WITH ME

HENRY F. LYTE   WILLIAM H. MONK

Eventide, four 10s

THERE ARE many conflicting stories as to both words and music of this beautiful hymn, and none can be verified. Lyte died soon after the hymn was written, in 1847, and it was not until 1861 that the music was composed. The hymn is in all hymnbooks. It is a moving and tender poem that compares with anything in the English language. Its metaphorical suggestions can be found in LUKE 24:29, "Abide with us, for it is toward evening."

1. A - bide with me! Fast
2. Swift to its close ebbs
3. I need Thy pre - sence
4. Hold Thou Thy cross be -

falls the e - ven - tide,
out life's lit - tle day,
ev - 'ry pass - ing hour,
fore my clos - ing eyes;

The dark - ness deep - ens,
Earth's joys grow dim, its
What but Thy grace can
Shine thro' the gloom and

Lord, with me a - bide!
glo - ries pass a - way;
foil the tempt - er's pow'r?
point me to the skies;

When oth - er help - ers
Change and de - cay in
Who, like Thy - self, my
Heav'n's morn - ing breaks and

fail, and com - forts flee, Help of the
all a - round I see; O Thou, who
guide and stay can be? Thro' cloud and
earth's vain shad - ows flee! In life, in

help - less, oh! a - bide with me!
chang - est not, a - bide with me!
sun - shine, oh, a - bide with me!
death, O Lord, a - bide with me!

241

PASS ME NOT, O GENTLE SAVIOUR

FANNY J. CROSBY

WILLIAM HOWARD DOANE

Pass Me Not, 8s, 5s.

FANNY JANE CROSBY was blind from the sixth week of her life, due to a physician's mistake. As a young woman she taught at the New York School for the Blind, where the secretary was Grover Cleveland. It was he who took down some of her first verses, and they became lifelong friends. The number of hymns written by Miss Crosby is estimated at 8,000. More than 500 are known to have been published, and many were signed Fanny C. Van Alstyne after she married Alexander Van Alstyne, a blind musician, when she was 38. As many as 60 of her hymns have been included in a single hymnal.

1. Pass me not, O gen - tle Sav - iour, Hear my hum - ble cry; While on oth - ers Thou art
2. Let me at Thy throne of mer - cy Find a sweet re - lief; Kneel - ing there in deep con-
3. Thou the spring of all my com - fort, More than life to me, Whom have I on earth be -

call - ing, Do not pass me by.
tri - tion, Help my un - be - lief.
side Thee? Whom in heav'n but Thee?

CHORUS

Sav - iour, Sav - iour, Hear my hum - ble

cry; While on oth - ers Thou art

call - ing, Do not pass me by.

JUST AS I AM

CHARLOTTE ELLIOT   WILLIAM B. BRADBURY

Woodworth, L.M.

AN INVALID for fifty years, Charlotte Elliot was inspired by the words, "Him that cometh to me I will in no wise cast out" (JOHN 6:37), to write a hymn dedicated to the handicapped and the unwanted. Her brother, a clergyman, was organizing a bazaar for the purpose of establishing a school. She wrote and published a hymn, hoping that the money she made would assist in the project. Needless to say, her offering brought in more money than a hundred bazaars.

1. Just as I am, with-out one plea, But
2. Just as I am, though tossed about With
3. Just as I am, Thou wilt re-ceive, Wilt

that Thy blood was shed for me, And that Thou bidd'st me
many a con-flict, many a doubt, Fightings and fears with-
wel-come, par-don, cleanse, re-lieve, Be-cause Thy prom-ise

come to Thee, O Lamb of God, I come! I come!
in, with-out, O Lamb of God, I come! I come!
I be-lieve, O Lamb of God, I come! I come!

JESUS CALLS US

Mrs. Cecil F. Alexander

William H. Jude

Galilee, 8.7.8.7.

This hymn is sung on St. Andrew's Day, November 30. It is also the adopted hymn of the St. Andrew Society of the United States and Canada. Strangely, the second stanza, which gave the poem its direct scriptural foundation, is no longer sung; the editors have been unable to ascertain the reason.

1. Je-sus calls us; o'er the tu-mult Of our life's wild, rest-less sea, Day by day His sweet voice sound-eth, Say-ing, "Chris-tian, fol-low Me."
2. Je-sus calls us from the wor-ship Of the vain world's gold-en store, From each i-dol that would keep us, Say-ing, "Chris-tian, love Me more."
3. Je-sus calls us: by Thy mer-cies, Sav-iour, may we hear Thy call, Give our hearts to Thy o-be-dience, Serve and love Thee best of all.

SAVIOUR, LIKE A SHEPHERD LEAD US

Ascribed to
Dorothy A. Thrupp
From Hymns for the Young, 1836   **William B. Bradbury**
Bradbury, 8s, 7s.

THOUGH IT IS probable that Miss Thrupp wrote this hymn, many authorities believe Henry Francis Lyte (of *Abide With Me*) is the author. It has been said that the text shows a preoccupation with the phrases of the Bible, the mark of the Evangelical. This would not aptly apply either to Lyte or Miss Thrupp. Bradbury wrote the tune expressly for his publication *Oriola,* a Sunday-school songbook.

1. Sav-iour, like a shep-herd lead us,
2. We are Thine; do Thou be - friend us,
3. Ear-ly let us seek Thy fa - vor;

Much we need Thy ten-der care;
Be the Guar - dian of our way;
Ear - ly let us do Thy will;

In Thy pleas - ant pas-tures feed us,
Keep Thy flock, from sin de - fend us,
Bless - ed Lord and on - ly Sav - iour,

For our use Thy folds pre - pare:
Seek us when we go a - stray:
With Thy love our bos - oms fill:

Bless-ed Je-sus, Bless-ed Je-sus, Thou hast
Bless-ed Je-sus, Bless-ed Je-sus, Hear Thy
Bless-ed Je-sus, Bless-ed Je-sus, Thou hast

bought us, Thine we are; Bless-ed Je-sus, Bless-ed
chil-dren when they pray; Bless-ed Je-sus, Bless-ed
loved us, love us still; Bless-ed Je-sus, Bless-ed

Je-sus, Thou hast bought us, Thine we are.
Je-sus, Hear Thy chil - dren when they pray.
Je-sus, Thou hast loved us, love us still.

JESUS, LOVER OF MY SOUL

CHARLES WESLEY   SIMEON B. MARSH

Martyn, eight 7s.

HENRY WARD BEECHER said, "I would rather have written that hynm of Wesley's than have the fame of all the kings that ever sat on earth." This, in a prodigious total of 6,500 hymns, is the most famous of all that Wesley wrote. It has been translated into all languages and appears in virtually every hymnbook. The tune, though criticized by musicians for the monotony of its inner voices, is nevertheless unfailing in its appeal, due to the beauty and simplicity of the melody and its easy range of a sixth.

1. Je - sus, Lov - er of my soul,
2. Oth - er ref - uge have I none;
3. Plen - teous grace with Thee is found,

Let me to Thy bo-som fly, While the near-er
Hangs my help-less soul on Thee; Leave, ah! leave me
Grace to cleanse from ev-'ry sin; Let the heal-ing

wa - ters roll, While the tem-pest still is high!
not a-lone, Still sup-port and com-fort me!
streams a-bound, Make and keep me pure with - in.

248

Hide me, O my Sav-iour, hide,
All my trust on Thee is stayed;
Thou of life the foun-tain art;

Till the storm of life is past;
All my help from Thee I bring;
Free-ly let me take of Thee;

Safe in-to the ha-ven guide,
Cov-er my de-fense-less head
Spring Thou up with-in my heart,

Oh re-ceive my soul at last!
With the shad-ow of Thy wing.
Rise to all e-ter-ni-ty.

ALL HAIL THE POWER OF JESUS' NAME

EDWARD PERRONET

OLIVER HOLDEN

Coronation, C.M.

THE REVEREND MR. PERRONET disagreed with the Wesley brothers, for whom he had preached and written hymns. John Wesley officially banned Perronet's hymns from the hymnal. But Perronet continued to write anonymously, and one day Oliver Holden, the American carpenter-composer, found these verses in an English magazine. He found that they fitted his new tune perfectly, and the great hymn was born that was to become a universal favorite, especially among the Methodists!

1. All hail the pow'r of
2. Let ev - 'ry kin - dred,
3. Oh, that with yon - der

Je - sus' name! Let an-gels pros - trate
ev - 'ry tribe, On this ter - res - trial
sa - cred throng We at His feet may

fall; Bring forth the roy - al
ball, To Him all maj - es -
fall; We'll join the ev - er -

di - a - dem, And crown Him
ty__ as - cribe, And crown Him
last - ing song, And crown Him

Lord of__ all; Bring forth the roy - al
Lord of__ all; To Him all maj - es -
Lord of__ all; We'll join the ev - er -

di - a - dem, And crown Him Lord__ of all.
ty as-cribe, And crown Him Lord__ of all.
last-ing song, And crown Him Lord__ of all.

STAND UP! STAND UP FOR JESUS

GEORGE DUFFIELD   GEORGE J. WEBB

Webb, 7.6.7.6.D.

GEORGE DUFFIELD'S friend, the Reverend Dudley Tyng, caught an arm in a corn-shelling machine, and it was torn off. A few days later, he lay dying in awful pain. It was during the great revival of 1858, in Philadelphia, and several ministers were at his bedside. When one of them asked Tyng if he wished to send a message to his parishioners, he said, "Tell them, 'Let us all stand up for Jesus'." The next Sunday Mr. Duffield preached from the text of EPHESIANS 6:14, after which was sung the hymn inspired by Tyng's dying words.

1. Stand up! stand up for Je-sus, Ye sol-diers of the Cross! Lift high His roy-al ban-ner, It must not suf-fer loss. From

2. Stand up! stand up for Je-sus! Stand in His strength a-lone; The arm of flesh will fail you, Ye dare not trust your own. Put

3. Stand up! stand up for Je-sus! The strife will not be long; This day the noise of bat-tle, The next the vic-tor's song. To

252

vic - t'ry un - to vic - t'ry His
on the Gos - pel ar - mor, Each
him that o - ver - com - eth A

ar - my shall He lead Till ev - 'ry foe is
piece put on with pray'r; Where du - ty calls or
crown of life shall be; He with the King of

van - quished And Christ is Lord in - deed.
dan - ger, Be nev - er want - ing there.
Glo - ry Shall reign e - ter - nal - ly.

FAIREST LORD JESUS

ANONYMOUS (c. 1677)

COMPOSER UNKNOWN
Arranged by R. S. WILLIS

Crusaders' Hymn
5.6.8.5.5.8

SINCE THIS hymn did not appear until the 17th century, it is hard to say why it is called "the crusaders' hymn." It is most probably of Silesian peasant origin, dealing simply and beautifully with the effects of nature and their symbolism in religion. John Julian states that it was "taken down from oral recitation in the district of Glaz." Glaz is not far from Prague, the home of John Hus. The flight of the Hussites from Bohemia may have provided an association with the Crusades.

1. Fair - est Lord Je - sus, Rul - er of all na - ture, O Thou of God and man the Son, Thee will I
2. Fair are the mead - ows, Fair - er still the wood - lands, Robed in the bloom - ing garb of spring; Je - sus is
3. Fair is the sun - shine, Fair - er still the moon - light, And all the twink - ling, star - ry host; Je - sus shines

254

cher - ish,	Thee will I hon - or,
fair - er,	Je - sus is pur - er,
bright - er,	Je - sus shines pur - er,

Thou, my soul's glo - ry, joy, and crown.
Who make the woe - ful heart to sing.
That all the an - gels heav'n can boast.

Beautiful Saviour

THIS TRANSLATION by J. A. Seiss of the same German original *(schönster Herr Jesu)* as FAIREST LORD JESUS was voted the second-favorite hymn of Lutherans in 1965 (behind *Holy, holy, holy!*). The Lutheran Hymnal traces the tune to a Silesian folk song. The Seiss translation is:

1. Beautiful Saviour,
   King of Creation,
   Son of God and Son of Man!
   Truly I'd love Thee,
   Truly I'd serve Thee,
   Light of my soul, my joy,
     my crown.

2. Fair are the meadows,
   Fair are the woodlands,
   Robed in the flow'rs of blooming
     spring;
   Jesus is fairer,
   Jesus is purer,
   He makes our sorrowing spirit
     sing.

3. Fair is the sunshine,
   Fair is the moonlight,
   Bright the sparkling stars on
     high;
   Jesus shines brighter,
   Jesus shines purer
   Than all the angels in the sky.

4. Beautiful Saviour,
   Lord of the nations,
   Son of God and Son of Man!
   Glory and honour,
   Praise, adoration,
   Now and for evermore be Thine!

LOVE DIVINE

CHARLES WESLEY

JOHN ZUNDEL

Beecher, 8.7.8.7.D.

HERE is the personalized God, pervading all human affairs: "He that loveth not knoweth not God; for God is Love" (1 JOHN 4:8). Wesley wrote his hymn during days when England was suffering a moral and religious recession. John Zundel was organist at Plymouth Church, Brooklyn, during the pastorate of Henry Ward Beecher. His musical standard was so high that it was not uncommon to hear: "We are going to hear Beecher and Zundel."

1. Love Di-vine, all love ex-cell-ing,
2. Breathe, O breathe Thy lov-ing Spir-it
3. Fin-ish, then, Thy new cre-a-tion;

Joy of heav'n, to earth come down; Fix in us Thy
In-to ev-'ry troub-led breast; Let us all in
Pure and spot-less let us be: Let us see Thy

hum-ble dwell-ing, All Thy faith-ful mer-cies crown:
Thee in-her-it, Let us find the prom-ised rest;
great sal-va-tion Per-fect-ly re-stored in Thee;

Je - sus, Thou art all com - pas-sion,
Take a - way the love of sin-ning;
Chang'd from glo - ry in - to glo - ry

Pure, un-bound-ed love Thou art; Vis-it us with
Al-pha and O - me - ga be; End of faith, as
Till in heav'n we take our place, Till we cast our

Thy sal-va-tion, En-ter ev -'ry trembling heart.
its be-gin-ing, Set our hearts at lib - er - ty.
crowns be-fore Thee, Lost in won - der, love, and praise.

257

MY FAITH LOOKS UP TO THEE

RAY PALMER   LOWELL MASON

Olivet, 6.6.4.6.6.6.4.

THE STORY is best told in the author's own words: "A year or two after the hymn was written . . . Dr. Mason met the author in the street in Boston, and asked him to furnish some hymns for a Hymn and Tune Book, which . . . he was about to publish . . . A copy was made and given to him, which, without much notice, he put into his pocket . . . Two or three days later we met again in the street, when, scarcely waiting to salute the writer, he earnestly exclaimed: 'Mr. Palmer, you may live many years and do many things, but I think you will be best known to posterity as the author of MY FAITH LOOKS UP TO THEE'."

1. My faith looks up to Thee,
2. May Thy rich grace im-part
3. While life's dark maze I tread,
4. When ends life's tran-sient dream,

Thou Lamb of Cal - va - ry,
Strength to my faint - ing heart,
And griefs a - round me spread,
When death's cold, sul - len stream

Sav - iour di - vine! Now hear me
My zeal in - spire; As Thou hast
Be Thou my guide; Bid dark-ness
Shall o'er me roll; Blest Sav - iour,

while I pray, Take all my
died for me, Oh may my
turn to day, Wipe sor - row's
then, in love, Fear and dis -

guilt a - way, Oh let me
love to Thee Pure, warm and
tears a - way, Nor let me
trust re - move; Oh bear me

from this day Be whol - ly Thine!
change-less be, A liv - ing fire!
ev - er stray From Thee a - side.
safe a - bove, A ran - somed soul!

O LOVE THAT WILT NOT LET ME GO

GEORGE MATHESON   ALBERT L. PEACE

St. Margaret, 8.8.8.8.6.

THIS HYMN, of Scottish origin, combines the elements of praise with the language of lyric poetry. The author wrote: "This came like a dayspring from on high. I have never been able to gain once more the same fervor in verse." Matheson was at the time going blind, of which he was well aware. The second stanza points out this distressing fact. The music by the organist Albert Peace is a perfect complement to the poem. Originally written as a gospel song, this hymn has found favor among the strictest purists, and is included in almost all church hymnals.

1. O Love that wilt not let me go, I rest my weary soul in
2. O Joy that seek-est me thro' pain, I can-not close my heart to
3. O Cross that lift-est up my head, I dare not ask to fly from

go,— I rest my wea-ry soul in
pain,— I can-not close my heart to
head, I dare not ask to fly from

Thee;   I give Thee back the life I
Thee;   I trace the rain-bow thro' the
Thee;   I lay in dust life's glo - ry

owe, That in Thine o - cean depths its
rain, And feel the pro - mise is not
dead, And from the ground there blos-soms

flow May rich - er, full - er___ be.
vain That morn shall tear - less___ be.
red Life that shall end - less___ be.

WHEN I SURVEY THE WONDROUS CROSS

Isaac Watts

Arranged by Lowell Mason
from the 1st Gregorian Tone

Hamburg, L.M.

Matthew Arnold considered this hymn the greatest in the English language. It was sung in church during the service he attended on the last Sunday of his life. On his deathbed he was heard to repeat the lines of the third stanza. George Eliot, evidently drawing upon an actual event, incorporates it in the death-bed scene of old Dinah Morris, in which she recites the hymn.

1. When I sur - vey the__ won - drous__ cross, On which the Prince of__ Glo - ry__ died,
2. For - bid it Lord, that__ I should__ boast, Save in the death of__ Christ, my__ God;
3. See, from His head, His__ hands, His__ feet, Sor - row and love flow__ min - gled__ down;
4. Were the whole realm of__ na - ture__ mine, That were a pres - ent__ far too__ small;

My rich - est gain I ____
All the vain things that__
Did e'er such love and__
Love so a - maz - ing,__

count but_ loss, And pour con -
charm me_ most, I sac - ri -
sor - row_ meet, Or thorns com -
so di - vine, De - mands my

tempt on all my_ pride.
fice them to His_ blood.
pose so rich a_ crown?
soul, my life, my_ all.

WHERE CROSS THE CROWDED WAYS OF LIFE

FRANK MASON NORTH

WILLIAM GARDINER'S
Sacred Melodies

Germany, L.M.

DOCTOR NORTH based his hymn on MATTHEW 22:9, "Go ye there-fore into the highways," which is more accurately, as in the Revised Version, ". . . . the parting of the highways." It is a mis-sionary hymn, dedicated to the problem of slum dwellers in large cities, and to the social aspect of religion. In *Time* magazine, Dec. 30, 1946, Marian Anderson said: ". . . Christianity may conceivably become the living faith of a dying civilization for the second time."

1. Where cross the crowd-ed ways_ of life, Where sound the cries of
2. In haunts of wretch-ed-ness_ and need, On shad-owed thresh-olds
3. From ten-der child-hood's help-less-ness, From wo-man's grief, man's
4. The cup of wa-ter given_ for Thee Still holds the fresh-ness
5. O Mas-ter, from the moun-tain-side, Make haste to heal these
6. Till sons of men shall learn_Thy love, And fol-low where Thy

race__ and clan, A - bove the
dark__ with fears, From paths where
bur - dened toil, From fam - ished
of__ Thy grace; Yet long these
hearts__ of pain; A - mong these
feet__ have trod; Till glo - rious

noise__ of self - ish strife,__ We
hide__ the lures of greed,__ We
souls,__ from sor - row's stress,__ Thy
mul - ti - tudes to see__ The
rest - less throngs a - bide,__ O
from__ Thy heaven a - bove,__ Shall

hear Thy voice,__ O Son__ of man.
catch the vi - sion of__ Thy tears.
heart has nev - er known re - coil.
sweet com - pas - sion of__ Thy face.
tread the cit - y's streets a - gain.
come the Cit - y of__ our God.

ONWARD, CHRISTIAN SOLDIERS

Sabine Baring-Gould   Arthur Sullivan
St. Gertrude, 6.5.6.5.D.

IT HAS BEEN SAID that Baring-Gould has more titles listed in the British Museum catalog than any of his contemporaries. He wrote a novel a year for more than 50 years. ONWARD, CHRISTIAN SOLDIERS was written in one night, in preparation for a children's parade. The original title was *Hymn for Procession with Cross and Banners*, and the text is figurative (following EPHESIANS 6:12, "we wrestle not against flesh and blood"). The musical setting by Sir Arthur Sullivan, although not the original one, has become universally accepted.

1. Onward, Christian sol-diers, Marching as to war,
2. Like a might-y ar-my Moves the church of God,
3. Onward, then, ye faith-ful, Join the hap-py throng,

With the cross of Je - sus Go-ing on be-fore.
Brothers we are tread-ing Where the saints have trod.
Blend with ours your voi - ces in the tri-umph song.

Christ, the roy-al Mas - ter, leads a-gainst the foe.
We are not di - vi - ded All one bod-y we.
Glo - ry, laud, and hon - or Un-to Christ the King.

Forward in-to bat-tle__ See, His ban-ners go!
One in hope and doc-trine__ One in char-i - ty.
This thro' count-less a - ges__ Men and an-gels sing.

CHORUS

On-ward, Christ-ian sol - diers,__

March-ing as to__ war, With the cross of

Je - sus Go -ing on be - fore.

FROM GREENLAND'S ICY MOUNTAINS

SEBASTIAN YRADIER   Missionary Hymn (Heber)   LOWELL MASON

BISHOP HEBER's *Holy, Holy, Holy* and Dr. Mason's *Nearer, My God, To Thee* may have proved more important in the catalogs of their respective authors, but the combination of their talents in this time-honored hymn has made a unique contribution. Protestant missionaries the world over have considered it their "theme song" since the 1820s. The Heber words were written in 1819, the Mason music in 1824, and by 1828 at the latest the combined effort had been internationally adopted. Dr. Mason originally christened his tune *Heber* in honor of the author, whom he never met.

1. From Green-land's i - cy moun - tains, From In-dia's co-ral strand, Where Af-ric's sun-ny foun-tains Roll
2. Can we, whose souls are light-ed By wis-dom from on high, Can we to men be-night-ed The
3. Waft, waft, ye winds, His sto - ry, And you, ye wa-ters, roll,_ Till, like a sea of glo-ry, It

268

down their gold-en sand; From many an an-cient
lamp of life de-ny? Sal - va-tion! O sal-
spreads from pole to pole: Till o'er our ran-som'd

riv - er, From many a palm - y
va - tion! The joy - ful sound pro -
na - ture The Lamb, for sin - ners

plain,— They call us to de -
claim,— Till earth's re - mot - est
slain,— Re - deem - er, King, Cre -

liv - er Their land from er-ror's chain.
na - tion Has learn'd Mes - si - ah's name.
a - tor, In bliss re - turns to reign.

269

WONDERFUL WORDS OF LIFE

PHILIP P. BLISS

Words of Life,
8.6.8.6.6.6. with refrain

LIKE ABRAHAM LINCOLN, Philip Bliss was born in a log cabin. In his boyhood he was always starved for music. As a young man he was employed by the famous musician George F. Root, later joining the staff of D. W. Whittle, the evangelist. All the royalties ($30,000) from his book *Gospel Songs* were donated to that cause. In a railway accident at Ashtabula, Ohio, in 1876, Bliss managed to escape from the wreck but died trying to rescue his wife.

1. Sing them o-ver a-gain to me,
2. Christ, the bless-ed One, gives to all,
3. Sweet-ly ech-o the gos-pel call,

Won-der-ful words of Life;—
Won-der-ful words of Life;—
Won-der-ful words of Life;—

Let me more of their beau-ty see,
Sin-ner, list to the lov-ing call,
Of-fer par-don and peace to all,

Won-der-ful words of Life.— Words of life and
Won-der-ful words of Life.— All so free-ly
Won-der-ful words of Life.— Je - sus, on - ly

beau - ty, Teach me faith— and du - ty:
giv - en, Woo-ing us— to heav - en:
Sav - iour, Sanc - ti - fy— for - ev - er:

CHORUS

Beau - ti - ful words, won-der - ful words,

won-der-ful words of Life;— Beau-ti-ful words,

won-der-ful words, won-der-ful words of Life!—

271

I WILL SING THE WONDROUS STORY

FRANCIS H. ROWLEY

PETER P. BILHORN

8.7.8.7., with refrain

THIS HYMN was first published in Ira D. Sankey's *Sacred Songs and Solos*, with revisions to which Rowley later objected. The revisions still appear in most hymnals, however. The first and final stanzas here are in their original form; the second is in the altered form. Rowley wrote the hymn at the suggestion of Peter Bilhorn, a young Swiss, during his pastorate in North Adams, Mass. Later he raised money to build the Angell Memorial Hospital for animals in Boston, and became its superintendent.

1. I will sing the wondrous story Of the Christ who died for me, How He left His home in glo - ry, For the cross on Cal - va - ry.

2. I was lost, but Je - sus found me, Found the sheep that went a - stray, Threw His lov-ing arms a - round me, Drew me back in - to His way.

3. He will keep me till the riv - er Rolls its wa - ters at my feet; Then He'll bear me safe - ly o - ver, Where the lov'd ones I shall meet.

CHORUS

Yes, I'll sing the won-drous sto ry Of the Christ who died for me, who died for me, Sing it with the Saints in glo ry, Gath-er'd by the crys-tal sea.

Yes, I'll sing the won-drous sto-ry Of the Christ who died for me, Sing it with the Saints in glo-ry Gath-er'd by the crys-tal sea, the crys-tal sea.

I LOVE TO TELL THE STORY

KATHERINE HANKEY   WILLIAM G. FISCHER

Brocton,
7s, 6s, with refrain

THIS HYMN was part of a long poem about the life of Jesus. Miss Hankey was a successful writer on religious subjects and a member of the Clapham sect, an evangelistic order. The tune, written by William Fischer, became a favorite of the Moody and Sankey revival meetings, and the composer once led a thousand-voice choir during a meeting in Philadelphia. He was a prolific composer of gospel hymns.

1. I love to tell the sto - ry Of un-seen things a - bove, Of Je - sus and His Glo - ry, Of_ Je - sus and His love! I

2. I love to tell the sto - ry, More won-der-ful_ it seems, Than all the gold-en fan - cies, Of_ all our gold-en dreams, I

3. I love to tell the sto - ry, For those who know it best. Seem hun-ger-ing and thirst-ing To_ hear it like the rest; And

love to tell the sto-ry, Be-cause I know it's true: It
love to tell the sto-ry, It did so much for me And
when in scenes of glo-ry, I sing the new, new song 'Twill

sat-is-fies my long-ings, As noth-ing else would do.
that is just the rea-son, I tell it now to thee.
be the old, old sto-ry that I have loved so long.

CHORUS

I love to tell the sto-ry! 'Twill be my theme in glo-ry, To

tell the old, old sto-ry of Je-sus and His love.

COME YE SINNERS, POOR AND NEEDY

JOSEPH HART   JEAN J. ROUSSEAU

Greenville, 8s, 7s.

ACCORDING to his own admission, Joseph Hart's early life was a "curious mixture of loose conduct . . . and endeavors after amendment of life." Certainly some of the spiritual conflict in his early life may have caused him to turn to the passage in MATTHEW 11:28, "Come unto me, all ye that labour and are heavy laden, and I will give you rest."

1. Come, ye sin-ners poor and need-y,
2. Let not con-science make you lin-ger,
3. Come, ye wear-y, heav-y lad-en,

Weak and wound-ed, sick and sore;
Nor of fit-ness fond-ly dream;
Bruised and man-gled by the fall;

Je-sus read-y stands to save you,
All the fit-ness He re-quir-eth
If you tar-ry till you're bet-ter

Full of pit-y, love and power:
Is to feel your need of Him:
You will nev-er come at all;

He is a - ble, He is a - ble,
This He gives you, This He gives you,
Not the right - eous, Not the right-eous,

He is will - ing, doubt no more.
'Tis the Spir - it's glim - m'ring beam.
Sin - ners Je - sus came to call.

277

THE LITTLE BROWN CHURCH
IN THE VALE

WILLIAM S. PITTS

IS IT A HYMN or a sectarian song? It certainly has a religious motif, and it appears in many nonsectarian hymnals. It is said that William S. Pitts encountered, in Iowa, the precise setting as pictured in the song; and in 1865 he wrote words and music.

1. There's a church in the val-ley by the wild-wood, No
2. How sweet on a bright Sabbath morn-ing To

lov-li-er place in the dale; No spot is so dear to my
list to the clear ring-ing bell; Its tones so sweet-ly are

child-hood As the lit-tle brown church in the vale.
call-ing, O come to the church in the vale.

O come   Come to the church in the
O come, come, come, come, come, come, come, come,

wild - wood, O come to the church in the
come, come, come, come, come, come, come, come,

dale; come No} spot is so dear to my
come, come, come, No}

child-hood As the lit - tle brown church in the vale.

BLESSED ASSURANCE

FANNY J. CROSBY

MRS. JOSEPH F. KNAPP

Blessed Assurance,
9.10.9.9., with refrain

FANNY J. CROSBY, the blind hymn-writer and teacher, had marvelous facility. When she first heard Mrs. Knapp play the tune of this hymn, in 1890, she sat down and within two hours completed the verses. She wrote, altogether, about 8,000 hymns and pious songs, using more than a hundred names. BLESSED ASSURANCE may have been suggested by JOHN 6:47, "He that believeth in Me hath everlasting life."

1. Bless - ed as-sur-ance, Je-sus is
2. Per - fect sub-mis-sion, all is at

mine! Oh, what a fore-taste of glo-ry di-
rest, I in my Sav-iour am hap-py and

vine! Heir of sal - va-tion, pur-chase of
blest, Watch-ing and wait-ing, look-ing a-

God, Born of His Spir-it, washed in His blood.
bove, Filled with His goodness, lost in His love.

CHORUS

This is my sto-ry, this is my

song, Prais-ing my Sav-iour all the day

long; This is my sto-ry, this is my

song, Prais-ing my Sav-iour all the day long.

TAKE THE NAME OF JESUS WITH YOU

LYDIA BAXTER   WILLIAM H. DOANE

8.7.8.7., with refrain

A LIFELONG Baptist, and contributor to collections for Sunday schools and evangelists, Lydia Baxter wrote many hymns. No fewer than five were included in Ira D. Sankey's *Sacred Songs and Solos,* and she herself published *Gems by the Wayside.* This is the only one of her hymns that has survived to any extent. It is included in most hymnals.

1. Take the name of Je-sus with you,
2. Take the name of Je-sus ev - er,
3. At the name of Je-sus bow - ing,

Child of sor - row and of woe;
As a shield from ev - 'ry snare;
Fall - ing pros - trate at His feet,

It will joy and com - fort give you,
If temp-ta - tions round you gath - er,
King of kings in heav'n we'll crown Him,

Take it, then, wher - e'er you go.
Breathe that ho - ly name in prayer.
When our jour - ney is com - plete.

CHORUS

Pre - cious name, O how
Pre-cious name,

sweet! Hope of earth and joy of heav'n;
O how sweet!

Pre - cious name, O how
Pre-cious name, O how

sweet!___ Hope of earth and joy of heav'n.
sweet, how sweet!

THAT OLD-TIME RELIGION

ANONYMOUS

Irregular, with refrain

No ONE KNOWS the origin of this famous old revival hymn. It was sung by the Jubilee Singers of Fisk University during the decade after the Civil War, and there is reason to believe that it was originally a spiritual. There are literally hundreds of versions, the one given here being the most commonly heard in the southern and southwestern United States. The editors attended a camp meeting in the Tennessee mountains during which THAT OLD-TIME RELIGION was sung continuously for three hours, accompanied by hand-clapping and stamping of the feet.

Give me that old-time re - li-gion, Give me that

old-time re - li-gion, Give me that old-time re-

li - gion, It's good e - nough for me!

1. It was good for the He-brew chil-dren, It was
2. It was good for__ Paul and Si-las, It was
3. It was good for the proph-et Dan-iel, It was
4. It is good when you are in trou-ble, It is
5. It will car-ry__ you to heav-en, It will

good for the He-brew chil-dren, It was good for the He-brew
good for__ Paul and Si-las, It was good for__ Paul and
good for the prophet Dan-iel, It was good for the proph-et
good when you are in trou-ble, It is good when you are in
car-ry__ you to heav-en, It will car-ry__ you to

D. C. al Fine

chil-dren, And it's good e-nough for me.
Si-las, And it's good e-nough for me.
Dan-iel, And it's good e-nough for me.
trou-ble, And it's good e-nough for me.
heav-en, And it's good e-nough for me.

WE'RE MARCHING TO ZION

ISAAC WATTS   ROBERT LOWRY

6.6.8.8.6.6., with refrain.

SIR ISAAC WATTS may have intended a stately and restrained mood, but the addition of a refrain by Lowry turned this hymn into a popular revival type, immediately accepted by the public. With his seemingly infallible instinct for pleasing the taste of the public, the Reverend Mr. Lowry could have been one of the most successful writers of popular songs in any period.

1. Come ye that love the Lord, And let your joys be known, Join in a song with sweet accord, Join in a song with sweet accord, And
2. The hill of Zi - on yields A thou-sand sa-cred sweets, Be - fore we reach the heav'n-ly fields, Be - fore we reach the heav'n-ly fields, Or
3. Then let our songs a - bound, And ev-'ry tear be dry; We're march-ing to Im-man-u-el's ground, We're march-ing to Im-man-u-el's ground, To

thus sur-round the throne, And thus sur-round the throne.
walk the gold-en streets, Or walk the gold-en streets.
fair-er worlds on high, To fair-er worlds on high.

CHORUS

We're march-ing to Zi - on, Beau-ti-ful, beau-ti-ful

Zi - on; We're march-ing up-ward to

Zi - on, The beau-ti-ful cit-y of God.__

SHALL WE GATHER AT THE RIVER?

ROBERT LOWRY

8.7.8.7, with refrain

A BAPTIST MINISTER, the Reverend Robert Lowry is a prominent writer of Sunday-school hymns, though he did not start to write until he was past 40. *Where Is My Wandering Boy Tonight?* was a tremendous "hit" of its time, and his collection *Bright Jewels* sold over a million copies; but Lowry seemed unaffected by success. He said that his greatest pleasure in life was "to preach a sermon to an appreciative congregation." This hymn emphasizes the possibility of mutual recognition in the hereafter.

1. Shall we gath-er at the riv-er,
2. On the mar-gin of the riv-er,
3. Ere we reach the shin-ing riv-er,

Where bright an-gel feet have trod,—
Wash-ing up its sil-ver spray,—
Lay we ev-'ry bur den down;—

With its crys-tal tide for - ev - er Flow-ing
We will walk and wor-ship ev - er, All the
Grace our spir-its will de - liv - er, And pro-

by the throne of God?
hap - py, gold - en day.
vide a robe and crown.

REFRAIN

Yes, we'll gath - er at the riv - er; The

beau - ti - ful, the beau - ti - ful riv - er;

Gath - er with the saints at the riv - er, That

flows by the throne of __ God.

289

TO THE WORK

FANNY J. CROSBY　　　　　　　　　　　　　**WILLIAM HOWARD DOANE**

Work Song,
12s, with refrain

For a busy industrialist, William H. Doane managed to do a lot of writing. Before he died he had written over 2,000 compositions, including song books, cantatas, and hymn tunes. It was he who introduced the work of Ira D. Sankey; he contributed many hymns to the famous Moody-Sankey cause, and wrote music for many Fanny Crosby hymns. He became a wealthy philanthropist, endowing the library of Denison University at Granville, Ohio.

1. To the work! to the work! we are servants of God, Let us follow the path that our Master has trod; With the balm of His counsel our strength to renew, Let us

2. To the work! to the work! let the hungry be fed; To the fountain of Life let the weary be led; In the cross of its banner our glory shall be, While we

3. To the work! to the work! in the strength of the Lord, And a robe and a crown shall our labor reward; When the home of the faithful our dwelling shall be, And we

do with our might what our hands find to do.
her-ald the ti-dings,"Sal - va-tion is free!"
shout with the ran-som'd "Sal - va-tion is free!"

CHORUS

Toil - ing on, Toil - ing

Toil - ing on,

on, Toil-ing on, Toil - ing

Toil-ing on, Toil-ing on,

on, Let us hope, Let us

Toil-ing on, and trust,

watch, And la-bor till the Mas-ter comes.

and pray,

291

SOFTLY AND TENDERLY
JESUS IS CALLING

WILL L. THOMPSON

Thompson,
11.7.11.7., with refrain

WILL THOMPSON wrote his first song at 16, and by the time he was 40 he had written several hits. Then he turned to hymn writing and opened a publishing house and a music store. He loaded a piano on a wagon and drove through the countryside singing his own hymns, perhaps anticipating the "song-pluggers" of 60 years later. When Thompson lay dying, the great Dwight L. Moody said to him, "Will, I would rather have written SOFTLY AND TENDERLY than anything I have been able to do in my whole life."

1. Soft - ly and ten-der-ly   Je-sus is call-ing,
2. Why should we tar-ry when Je-sus is plead-ing
3. Oh, for the won-der-ful   love He has prom-is'd,

Call - ing for you and for   me;—
Plead - ing for you and for   me?—
Prom - is'd for you and for   me;—

See   on the por - tals He's wait-ing and watch-ing,
Why should we lin - ger and heed not His mer-cies,
Tho' we have sinn'd He has mer-cy and par-don,

Watch - ing for you and for me.
Mer - cies for you and for me?
Par - don for you and for me.

CHORUS

mf

Come home,____ Come home,____
Come home, Come home,

cresc.

Ye who are wea - ry come home;____

a tempo

p Ear - nest - ly, ten - der - ly Je - sus is call - ing,

rit. *p*

Call - ing, O sin - ner, Come home.____

TRUST AND OBEY

J. H. SAMMIS   DANIEL B. TOWNER

6.6.9.6.6.8., with refrain

DOCTOR TOWNER was associated with Moody and Sankey, as a singer. In 1893 he was made director of the Moody Bible Institute of Chicago, where he remained until his death. He wrote many hymns, of which TRUST AND OBEY is the best known. The title was suggested to Sammis by Doctor Towner, who had heard a young man say, at a testimony meeting, "I am not sure, but I am going to trust and obey." This story is told in Ira Sankey's *Story of the Gospel Hymns*.

1. When we walk with the Lord In the
2. Not a shad-ow can rise, Not a
3. Not a bur-den we bear, Not a
4. Then in fel-low-ship sweet We will

Light of His Word What a glo-ry He
cloud in the skies, But His smile quick-ly
sor-row we share, But our toil He doth
sit at His feet, Or we'll walk by His

sheds on our way! While we do His good-
drives it a-way; Not a doubt or a
rich-ly re-pay; Not a grief nor a
side in the way; What He says we will

will, He a - bides with us still,
fear, Not a sigh nor a tear,
loss, Not a frown or a cross,
do, Where He sends we will go,

And with all who will trust and o - bey.
Can a - bide while we trust and o - bey.
But is blest if we trust and o - bey.
Nev - er fear, on - ly trust and o - bey.

CHORUS

Trust and o - bey, for there's no oth-er way To be

hap-py in Je-sus, But to trust and o - bey.

295

YIELD NOT TO TEMPTATION

HORATIO R. PALMER

Fortitude,
11.11.11.12., with refrain

DOCTOR PALMER himself wrote: "This song is an inspiration. I was at work on the dry subject of "Theory" (he wrote *A Theory of Music* in 1868) when the complete idea flashed upon me, and I laid aside the theoretical work and hurriedly penned both words and music as fast as I could write them . . . I am reverently thankful it has been a power for good."

1. Yield not to temp-ta-tion, For yielding is sin,
2. Shun e-vil com-pan-ions, Bad lan-guage dis-dain,
3. To him that o'er-com-eth God giv-eth a crown,

Each vic-t'ry will help you Some oth-er to win;
God's name hold in rev'rence, Nor take it in vain;
Thro' faith we shall con-quer, Though of-ten cast down;

Fight man-ful-ly on-ward, Dark pas-sions sub-due,
Be thought-ful and ear-nest, Kind-heart-ed and true,
He who is our Sav-iour, Our strength will re-new,

Look ev-er to Je-sus, He'll car-ry you through.
Look ev-er to Je-sus, He'll car-ry you through.
Look ev-er to Je-sus, He'll car-ry you through.

CHORUS

Ask the Sa-viour to help you,

Com-fort, strength-en and keep you; He is will-ing to

aid you, He will car-ry you through.

WORK, FOR THE NIGHT IS COMING

ANNA LOUISE WALKER   LOWELL MASON

Work Song, P.M.

THIS HYMN was first published as a poem, in 1864. According to Ira D. Sankey, Miss Walker was inspired by Jesus' words: "I must work the works of Him That sent me, while it is day; the night cometh, when no man can work." (JOHN 9:4.) The tune is known in England as *Diligence*.

1. Work for the night is com - ing,
2. Work for the night is com - ing,

Work thro' the morn - ing hours:
Un - der the sun - set skies

Work while the dew is spark - ling
While their bright tints are glow - ing

Work 'mid spring - ing flow'rs;
Work, for day - light flies,

Work when the day grows bright - er
Work till the last beam fad - eth

Work in the glow - ing sun;
Fad - eth to shine no more;

Work, for the night is com - ing
Work while the night is dark'n - ing

When man's work is done.
When man's work is o'er.

BRINGING IN THE SHEAVES

Knowles Shaw

George A. Minor

12.11.12.11., with refrain

Here is a text from Matthew 13:30, "The harvest is the end of the world." We are admonished to prepare our lives by thought and deed so that at the end there may be a time of rejoicing, rather than sorrow for the recklessness with which we sometimes ignore the laws of nature and divine help.

1. Sow-ing in the morn-ing, sow-ing seeds of kind-ness,
2. Sow-ing in the sun-shine, sow-ing in the shad-ows,
3. Go-ing forth with weep-ing, sow-ing for the Mas-ter,

Sow-ing in the noon-tide and the dew-y eves;
Fear-ing nei-ther clouds nor win-ter's chil-ling breeze;
Tho' the loss sus-tained our spir-it oft-en grieves;

Wait-ing for the har-vest, and the time of reap-ing,
By and by the har-vest, and the la-bor end-ed,
When our weep-ing's o-ver, He will bid us wel-come,

300

We shall come, re-joic-ing, bring-ing in the sheaves.
We shall come, re-joic-ing, bring-ing in the sheaves.
We shall come, re-joic-ing, bring-ing in the sheaves.

CHORUS

Bring-ing in the sheaves, bring-ing in the sheaves,

We shall come, re-joic-ing, Bring-ing in the sheaves;

Bring-ing in the sheaves, bring-ing in the sheaves,

We shall come, re-joic-ing, bring-ing in the sheaves.

THE DAY THOU GAVEST, LORD, IS ENDED

JOHN ELLERTON   CLEMENT C. SCHOLEFIELD

St. Clement, 9.8.9.8

QUEEN VICTORIA chose this hymn for her Diamond Jubilee in 1897. The expanding British Empire must have found symbolic parallels in the sentiment contained in the second verse, but the hymn would be better confined to its original intention— that of a missionary hymn, expressing the movement of the Church to all parts of the world.

1. The day Thou gav-est,
2. As o'er each con-ti-
3. So be it, Lord; Thy

Lord, is end-ed, The dark-ness
nent and is-land The dawn leads
throne shall nev-er, Like earth's proud

falls at Thy be-hest; To
on an-oth-er day, The
em-pires, pass a-way; Thy

Thee our morn - ing hymns as -
voice of prayer is nev - er
king - dom stands, and grows for -

cend - ed, Thy praise___ shall
si - lent, Nor dies___ the
ev - er, Till all___ Thy

sanc - ti - fy___ our rest.
strain of praise___ a - way.
crea - tures own___ Thy sway.

REVIVE US AGAIN

WILLIAM PATON MACKAY   JOHN J. HUSBAND
11s, with refrain

THIS IS one of the most powerful "camp meeting" hymns of all time.
The origin of the tune is very hard to trace, but it was almost
certainly written by John Husband, a Philadelphia musician of the
period after the American Revolution. It has been used also for the
folk song *Hallelujah! I'm a Bum!* historically associated with the
I.W.W.

1. We praise Thee O God! for the Son of Thy love, For__ Je-sus Who died and is now gone a-bove.
2. We praise Thee O God! for Thy Spir-it of light, Who has shown us our Sa-vior, and scat-tered our night.
3. All glo-ry and praise to the Lamb that was slain, Who has borne all our sins and hath cleansed ev-'ry stain.
4. Re-vive us a-gain; fill each heart with Thy love; May each soul be re-kin-dled with fire from a-bove.

CHORUS

Hal - le - lu - jah! Thine the glo - ry, Hal - le - lu - jah! A - men. Hal - le - lu - jah! Thine the glo - ry, Re - vive us a - gain.

305

AMAZING GRACE

JOHN NEWTON   SAMUEL STANLEY

Warwick, C.M.

THE EARLY LIFE of John Newton was anything but exemplary. He deserted from the British Navy, and was publicly whipped when caught. Then he became captain of a slave ship, brutal and merciless. His conversion came after a storm almost destroyed him and his human cargo. He educated himself, and after twelve years was ordained a minister. He became a friend of William Cowper, and in 1779 the two men published the *Olney Hymns,* "for the use of plain people."

1. A - maz - ing____ grace, how____ sweet____ the sound, That saved a____
2. 'Twas grace that____ taught my____ heart____ to fear, And grace my____
3. Thro' man - y____ dan - gers,____ toils____ and snares, I have al -
4. Yes, when this____ heart and____ flesh____ shall fail, And mor - tal____

soul___ like___ me! I
fears___ re - lieved; How
read - y___ come; 'Tis
life___ shall___ cease, I

once___ was___ lost, but___
pre - cious___ that___ did
grace___ that___ brought
shall___ pos - sess with -

now___ am___ found: Was
grace___ ap - pear, The
safe___ thus___ far, And
in___ the___ vail, A

blind but_ now I_ see.___
hour I_ first be - lieved.___
grace will lead me_ home.___
life_ of_ joy and_ peace.___

307

INTO THE WOODS MY MASTER WENT

Sidney Lanier

Peter C. Lutkin

Lanier, P. M.

THE ORIGINAL TITLE of Lanier's poem was *A Ballad of Trees and the Master.* It appeared in a volume of his poems that was published posthumously. Lanier lectured at John Hopkins University on "The Interrelation of Music and Poetry," and played first flute with the Peabody Symphony Orchestra of Baltimore, in 1873. He had contracted tuberculosis as a result of imprisonment during the Civil War, and was slowly dying. Here he considers Jesus' last thoughts in the Garden of Gethsemane. INTO THE WOODS MY MASTER WENT was written in 1880, and Lanier died the following year, at the age of 39. His hymn is often sung on Good Friday.

1. In - to the woods my Mas - ter went,
2. Out of the woods my Mas - ter went, And

Clean for-spent, for - spent;   In - to the woods my
He was well con - tent;   Out of the woods my

Mas - ter came, For - spent with love and
Mas - ter came, Con - tent with death and

shame. But the ol - ives they were not
shame. When death and shame would

blind to Him, The lit-tle gray leaves were
woo Him last, From un-der the trees they

kind to Him, The thorn tree had a
drew Him last, 'Twas on a tree they

mind to Him, When in-to the woods He came.
slew Him last, When out of the woods He came.

THE NINETY AND NINE

ELIZABETH C. CLEPHANE   IRA D. SANKEY

Ninety and Nine, Irregular

A POEM by a little Scottish girl was published in a Glasgow paper in 1876. It attracted the attention of Ira Sankey, the gospel singer, who was on tour with the evangelist Dwight L. Moody. Sankey cut the poem from the paper; a tune was taking form in his mind. When the sermon the next Sunday had as its text "the Good Shepherd," Sankey used it for his solo, although it had not yet been put on paper. The words and music were never changed.

1. There were nine-ty and nine that safe-ly lay In the shel-ter of the fold, But one was out on the
2. "Lord,— Thou hast here Thy nine-ty and nine; Are they not e-nough for Thee?" But the Shep-herd made an-swer:
3. But all thro' the moun-tains, thun-der-riv'n, And up from the rock-y steep, There a-rose a glad cry to the

hills a way, Far off from the gates of
"This of mine Has wan-dered a - way from
gate of heav'n, "Re - joice! I have found my

gold A - way on the moun - tains
me, And, al - though the road be
sheep!" And the an - gels ech-oed a -

wild and bare, A-way from the ten - der
rough and steep, I go to the des-ert to
round the throne, "Re-joice! for the Lord brings

Shepherd's care, A-way from the ten-der Shepherd's care.
find my sheep, I go to the desert to find my sheep.
back His own! Rejoice! for the Lord brings back His own!"

SINCE JESUS CAME INTO MY HEART

R. H. McDaniel

Charles H. Gabriel

12.8.12.8. with refrain

No TESTAMENT is more powerful than that of a gospel song when the congregation is moved by a communion of spiritual experience. Such an experience brought about the conversion of Policeman Fowler during a Billy Sunday revival in Philadelphia. Scores of other policemen later followed the example of Fowler.

1. What a won-der-ful change in my
2. I have ceased from my wand'ring and
3. There's a light in the val-ley of
4. I shall go there to dwell in that

life has been wrought Since Je-sus came in-to my
go-ing a-stray, Since Je-sus came in-to my
death now for me, Since Je-sus came in-to my
Cit-y, I know, Since Je-sus came in-to my

heart! I have light in my soul for which long I had sought,
heart! And my sins, which were man-y, are all washed a-way,
heart! And the gates of the Cit-y be-yond I can see,
heart! And I'm hap-py, so hap-py, as on-ward I go

Since Je-sus came in-to my heart!

CHORUS

Since Jesus came in-to my heart,   Since
Since Jesus came in, came in - to my heart, Since

Je-sus came in-to my heart,   Floods of
Je-sus came in, came in - to my heart,

joy o'er my soul like the sea bil-lows roll, Since

Je - sus came in - to my heart.

LOVE LIFTED ME

James Rowe   Howard E. Smith

Irregular, with refrain

THIS GOSPEL SONG was a favorite with the great evangelists of the early part of the 20th century, Billy Sunday and Gipsy Smith. It proved to have such vitality and power that their successor in spirit and effectiveness, Billy Graham, has used it in his revival campaigns nearly fifty years later.

1. I was sink - ing deep in sin,
2. All my heart to Him I give,
3. Souls in dan - ger look a - bove,

Far from the peace-ful shore, Ver-y deep-ly
Ev - er to Him I'll cling, In His bless - ed
Je - sus com-plete-ly saves; He will lift you

stained with - in, Sink-ing to rise no more;
pres - ence live, Ev - er His prais - es sing.
by His love Out of the an - gry waves.

But the Mas - ter of the sea Heard my de-spair-ing
Love so might - y and so true Mer - its my soul's best
He's the Mas - ter of the sea, Bil-lows His will o -

cry, From the wa-ters lift - ed me, Now safe am I.
songs; Faith-ful, lov-ing serv-ice, too, To Him be-longs.
bey; He your Sav-iour wants to be, Be saved to - day.

CHORUS

Love lift - ed me! Love lift - ed
e - ven me!

me! When noth - ing else could help,
e - ven me!

1. Love lift - ed me. 2. Love lift - ed me.

315

O HAPPY DAY

PHILIP DODDRIDGE   EDWARD F. RIMBAULT

L. M.

JAMES MONTGOMERY said: "Blessed is the man who can take the words of this hymn and make them his own experience." The Reverend Mr. Doddridge was a prolific writer of hymns, and a friend of the Wesleys. Edward Rimbault was a leading English composer. He was once asked to head the school of music at Harvard University, but did not accept the offer.

1. Oh, hap - py day, that fixed my choice On Thee, my Sav - iour and my God! Well may this glow - ing heart re -
2. 'Tis done, the great trans - ac - tion's done; I am my Lord's, and He is mine; He drew me, and I fol - lowed
3. High heav'n that hears the sol - emn vow, That vow re - newed shall dai - ly hear; Till in life's lat - est hour I

joice, And tell its rap-tures all a-broad.
on, Re-joiced to own the call Di-vine.
bow, And bless in death a bond so dear.

CHORUS

Hap-py day, hap-py day, When Je-sus

washed my sins a-way! He taught me how to watch and

pray, And live re-joic-ing ev-'ry day; Hap-py

day, hap-py day, When Je-sus washed my sins a-way!

BLEST BE THE TIE THAT BINDS

John Fawcett   Hans G. Naegeli

Dennis, S.M.

After several years of serving the poverty-stricken parish of Wainsgate, England, the Reverend Mr. Fawcett was called to a large church and a large salary; but his parishioners were so heartbroken, and the Fawcetts had become so attached to their friends, that they decided to stay. The following Sunday Fawcett preached from Luke 12:15, "A man's life consisteth not in the abundance of the things he possesseth," and then all joined in singing his new hymn, Blest be the tie that binds.

1. Blest be the tie that
2. Be - fore our Fa - ther's
3. We share our mu - tual
4. When we a - sun - der

binds   Our   hearts   in
throne, We   pour   our
woes,   Our   mu -   tual
part,   It   gives   us

Christ - ian   love;   The
ar - dent   pray'rs; Our
bur - dens   bear;   And
in - ward   pain;   But

fel - low - ship— of
fears,— our hopes,— our
oft - en for— each
we— shall still— be

kin - dred minds— Is
aims— are one,— Our
oth - er flows— The
joined— in heart,— And

like— to that— a - bove.
com - forts and— our cares.
sym - pa - thiz - ing tear.
hope— to meet— a - gain.

THE OLD RUGGED CROSS

GEORGE BENNARD

SAYS George W. Sanville, head of one of the world's most respected publishers of sacred songs, "Around the world, on radio, where it has been the most used gospel song, and in multitudinous religious meetings, this arrow of the gospel, shafted with music, has shot God's truth home to the hearts of men. It is the epitome of the gospel in song; it is in the world of gospel song what JOHN 3:16 is in gospel doctrine . . . the heart of it." Within thirty years of its publication, more than twenty million copies of THE OLD RUGGED CROSS had been sold—more than any other musical composition, of any kind, in all history.

1. On a hill far a-way stood an old rug-ged cross, The em-blem of suf-f'ring and shame; And I love that old cross where the

2. Oh, that old rug-ged cross, so de-spised by the world, Has a won-drous at-trac-tion for me; For the dear Lamb of God left His

3. To the old rug-ged cross I will ev - er be true, Its shame and re-proach glad-ly bear; Then He'll call me some day to my

dear-est and best For a world of lost sin-ners was slain.
glo-ry a-bove, To bear it to dark Cal-va-ry.
home far a-way, Where His glo-ry for-ev-er I'll share.

CHORUS

So I'll cher-ish the old rug-ged cross, the

cross, Till my tro-phies at last I lay
old rug-ged cross,

down; I will cling to the old rug-ged cross, the

cross, And ex-change it some day for a crown.
old rug-ged cross,

321

IN THE GARDEN

C. Austin Miles

In The Garden, irregular.

According to the author, he was working in his dark-room when the Bible fell open at John 20, the scene containing the account of Mary's meeting with Jesus. His senses prepared by the dim light, he saw the entire scene before him, as in a vision. He writes: "Under the inspiration of this vision I wrote as quickly as the words could be formed the poem exactly as it has since appeared. That same evening I wrote the music."

1. I come to the gar-den a-lone,— While the dew is still on the ros-es, And the voice I hear Fall-ing

2. He speaks, and the sound of His voice— Is so sweet the birds hush their sing-ing, And the mel-o-dy That He

3. I'd stay in the gar-den with Him— Tho' the night a-round me be fall-ing, But He bids me go; Thro' the

on my ear, The Son of God dis - clos - es.
gave to me With - in my heart is ring - ing.
voice of woe His voice to me is call - ing.

CHORUS

And He walks with me, and He talks with me, And He

tells me I am His own; And the joy we share as we

tar-ry there, None oth-er has ev-er___ known.

IN THE SWEET BYE-AND-BYE

S. Fillmore Bennett   Joseph P. Webster

L.M., with refrain

Joseph Philbrick Webster was a musician who settled in Elkhorn, Wis., in 1857. When Dr. Bennett also came to Elkhorn, the two collaborated on popular songs, and wrote several successful ones. One day, so the story goes, Webster was feeling glum. When asked what the trouble was, he replied, "Oh, everything will be all right—bye-and-bye." That gave the doctor an idea, and within an hour they had turned out a hymn. It was to be the only lasting song they wrote, and has even been flattered by the bitter parody of the I.W.W., "There'll be pie in the sky, bye-and-bye."

1. There's a land that is fair-er than
2. We shall sing on that beau-ti-ful
3. To our boun-ti-ful Fa-ther a-

day, And by faith we can see it a-
shore The mel-o-di-ous songs of the
bove, We will of-fer our trib-ute of

far; For the Fa-ther waits o-ver the
blest, And our spir-its shall sor-row no
praise For the glor-i-ous gift of His

way To pre-pare us a dwell-ing place there.
more, Not a sigh for the bless-ing of rest.
love, And the bless-ings that hal-low our days.

CHORUS

In the sweet bye-and-bye, we shall

In the sweet bye-and-bye

meet on that beau-ti-ful shore, In the sweet bye-and-

In the sweet bye-and-

bye we shall meet on that beau-ti-ful shore.

bye, bye-and-bye,

WHEN THE ROLL IS CALLED UP YONDER

JAMES M. BLACK

15.11.D., with refrain

JAMES BLACK called the Sunday school roll every week in Williamsport, Pa. But one Sunday he missed the answer of a little girl whom he had befriended. Then he heard that she was ill, and had little chance to live. He remembered the roll-call and wondered if he would be there to answer when the "great roll-call" is made. This hymn is seldom found in church hymnals, but is one of the best known of all gospel songs.

1. When the trum-pet of the Lord shall sound, and saved of earth shall ga-ther o - ver
2. On that bright and cloud-less morn-ing when the chos - en ones shall ga-ther to their
3. Let me la - bor for the Mas-ter from the all of life is o - ver, and my

time shall be no more, And the
on the oth - er shore, And the
dead in Christ shall rise, And the
home be - yond the skies, And the
dawn till set - ting sun, Let me
work on earth is done, And the

1.

morn-ing breaks, e - ter - nal, bright, and fair; When the
glo-ry of His res - ur - rec - tion share; When His
talk of all His won-drous love and care, Then when

roll is called up yon-der, I'll be there.
roll is called up yon-der, I'll be there.
roll is called up yon-der, I'll be there.

CHORUS

When the roll ___ is called up yon - der, When the
When the roll is called up yon-der I'll be there,

roll ___ is called up yon der, When the
When the roll is called up yon-der, I'll be there

roll ___ is called up yon-der, When the
When the roll

roll is called up yon-der I'll be there.

327

BEULAH LAND

EDGAR PAGE   L.M. with refrain   JOHN R. SWENEY

THE BIBLICAL ALLUSION is in Isaiah 62:4, taken from the Hebrew word meaning "married" in the sense of marital bliss; Beulah Land is used in the sense of the Promised Land, this time promised to the Hebrews after their return from the punitive exile in Babylon. John Bunyan used Beulah Land in a similar sense in *Pilgrim's Progress*. Of several hymns that have been written and set to music on the Beulah Land theme, this is the most legitimate; but almost equally popular is a rousing Sunday School song.

1. I've reached the land of corn and wine, And
2. My Sav-iour comes and walks with me, And
3. The zeph-yrs seem to float to me, Sweet

all its rich-es free-ly mine; Here shines un-dimmed one
sweet com-mun-ion here have we; He gen-tly leads me
sounds of Heav-en's mel-o-dy, As an-gels with the

bliss-ful day, For all my night has passed a-way.
by His hand, For this is Heav-en's bor-der-land.
white-robed throng Join in the sweet Re-demp-tion song.

CHORUS

O Beu-lah Land, sweet Beu-lah Land, As

on thy high-est mount I stand, I

look a-way a-cross the sea, Where

man-sions are pre-pared for me, And view the shin-ing

glo-ry-shore, My Heav'n, my home for-ev-er-more!

329

WILL THERE BE ANY STARS IN MY CROWN?

12.9.12.9. with refrain

E. E. HEWITT   JOHN R. SWENEY

JOHN R. SWENEY led an army band during the Civil War. Later he became a professor of music at the Pennsylvania Military Academy, and there he edited about 50 song collections. He often worked with William J. Kirkpatrick, and the team of Sweney and Kirkpatrick became well known. Mr. Hewitt, author of the words, was inspired by the text: "Ye shall receive a crown of glory that fadeth not away." 1 PETER 5:4.

1. I am think-ing to-day of that beau-ti-ful land I shall reach when the sun go-eth down; When through won-der-ful grace by my
2. In the strength of the Lord let me la-bor and pray, Let me watch as a win-ner of souls; That bright stars may be mine in the
3. Oh, what joy it will be when His face I be-hold, Liv-ing gems at His feet to lay down; It would sweet-en my bliss in the

Sav-iour I stand, Will there be an-y stars in my crown?
glo-ri-ous day, When His praise like the sea bil-low rolls.
cit-y of gold, Should there be an-y stars in my crown.

CHORUS

Will there be an-y stars, an-y stars in my crown When at

eve-ning the sun go-eth down? *go-eth down?* When I

wake with the blest In the man-sions of rest, Will there

be an - y stars in my crown? *in my crown?*

ALMOST PERSUADED

PHILIP P. BLISS

P.M.

ONE SUNDAY, in church, Philip Bliss was listening carefully while the sermon was in progress. The text was from ACTS 26:28, "Then Agrippa said to Paul, almost thou persuadest me to be a Christian." Then the preacher said, "To be almost saved is to be entirely lost!" This theme so impressed Bliss that he wrote ALMOST PERSUADED. For notes on Philip P. Bliss see *Wonderful Words of Life*, page 270.

1. "Al - most per - suad - ed," now to be - lieve;___ "Al - most per - suad - ed,"
2. "Al - most per - suad - ed," come, come to - day;___ "Al - most per - suad - ed,"
3. "Al - most per - suad - ed," har - vest is past!___ "Al - most per - suad - ed,"

Christ to re - ceive;____
turn not a - way;____
doom comes at last!____

Seems now some soul to say,
Je - sus in - vites you here,
"Al - most" can - not a - vail;

"Go, Spir - it, go Thy way, Some more con -
An - gels are ling'ring near, Pray'rs rise from
"Al-most" is but to fail! Sad, sad that

ven - ient day On Thee I'll call."
hearts so dear, O wan-d'rer, come.
bit - ter wail, "Al - most," but lost.__

HAVE THINE OWN WAY, LORD!

ADELAIDE A. POLLARD

GEORGE C. STEBBINS

5s, 4s.

A MODEST and self-effacing little woman, Adelaide Pollard practiced throughout her life the principle of Christian submission to the will of the Almighty. She wrote many hymns, but was too modest to sign her name to them. Constantly traveling from place to place, she devoted her life to the service of others. She died in a railroad station at the age of 72, while on her way to a preaching engagement.

1. Have Thine own way, Lord! Have Thine own way! Thou art the Pot - ter;
2. Have Thine own way, Lord! Have Thine own way! Wound - ed and wea - ry,
3. Have Thine own way, Lord! Have Thine own way! Hold o'er my be - ing

I am the clay.___
Help me, I pray!___
Ab - so - lute sway!___

Mould me and make me
Pow - er, all pow - er,
Fill with Thy Spir - it

Aft - er Thy will,___ While I am
Sure - ly is Thine!___ Touch me and
Till all shall see___ Christ on - ly,

wait - ing, Yield - ed and still.___
heal me, Sav - iour Di - vine!___
al - ways, Liv - ing in me!___

TAKE MY LIFE AND LET IT BE

Frances R. Havergal   H. A. Caesar Malan

Hendon, 7s.

Miss Havergal herself wrote, according to Percy Dearmer (in *Songs of Praise Discussed*): "I went for a little visit of five days. There were ten persons in the house (Areley House); some unconverted and long-prayed-for, some converted but not rejoicing Christians. He gave me the prayer 'Lord, give me all in this house!' and He just *did*. Before I left the house everyone had got a blessing." Romans 12:1 is usually associated with this hymn.

1. Take my life,— and— let it
2. Take my feet,— and— let them
3. Take my sil - ver— and my
4. Take my will,— and— make it

be Con - se - cra - ted,—
be Swift and beau - ti -
gold, Not a mite— would—
Thine, It shall be— no—

Lord, to— Thee; Take my
ful for— Thee; Take my
I with - hold; Take my
lon - ger— mine; Take my

hands, and let them move
voice, and let me sing,
mo - ments and my days,
heart, it is Thine own;

At the im - pulse of Thy love,
Al - ways, on - ly, for my King,
Let them flow in cease - less praise,
It shall be Thy roy - al throne,

At the im - pulse of Thy love.
Al - ways, on - ly, for my King.
Let them flow in cease - less praise.
It shall be Thy roy - al throne.

GOD WILL TAKE CARE OF YOU

MRS. C. D. MARTIN   W. S. MARTIN

8.6.8.6., with refrain

THE WORDS AND MUSIC of this hymn were written by the Reverend Mr. Martin and his wife. When she was in the hospital, to which she had been rushed for an emergency appendectomy, her only thought was of her husband, and when she saw his distraught expression, she said to him: "Never mind, dear, God will take care of you."

1. Be not dis-mayed what-e'er be-tide,
2. Thro' days of toil when heart doth fail,
3. No mat-ter what may be the test,

God will take care of you; Be-neath His wings of
God will take care of you; When dan-gers fierce your
God will take care of you; Lean, wea-ry one, up-

love a-bide, God will take care of you.
path as-sail, God will take care of you.
on His breast, God will take care of you.

339

WHERE HE LEADS ME I WILL FOLLOW

E. W. BLANDY   J. S. NORRIS

Where He Leads Me
8.8.8.7. with refrain

THIS WAS THE great revival song of Gipsy Smith, the famous evangelist. It is admirably suited to congregational singing, as the harmony parts lie easily for use without accompaniment. It has been impossible to find information concerning the writers. Blandy's name is usually misspelled "Blandly," and nothing is known about J. S. Norris.

1. I can hear my Sav - iour
2. I'll go with Him through the
3. He will give me grace and

call - ing,   I can hear my Sav - iour
judg-ment,   I'll go with Him through the
glo - ry,   He will give me grace and

call - ing,   I can hear my Sav - iour
judg-ment,   I'll go with Him through the
glo - ry,   He will give me grace and

call-ing, "Take thy cross and fol-low, fol-low me."
judg-ment, I'll go with Him, with Him all the way.
glo-ry, And go with me, with me all the way.

CHORUS

Where He leads me I will fol-low, Where He

leads me I will fol-low, Where He leads me I will

fol-low, I'll go with Him, with Him all the way.

HE LEADETH ME

JOSEPH H. GILMORE

WILLIAM B. BRADBURY

L.M., with refrain

ONE EVENING Joseph Gilmore was inspired to write a hymn. He gave it to his wife and forgot about it. She sent it to *The Watchman and Reflector*. Three years later Dr. Gilmore was in Rochester, N. Y. to preach. On entering the chapel he took up a hymnbook, thinking, "I wonder what they sing!" The book opened at HE LEADETH ME.

1. He lead-eth me: Oh, bless-ed thought!
2. Some-times 'mid scenes of deep-est gloom,
3. Lord, I would clasp Thy hand in mine,
4. And when my task on earth is done,

Oh, words with heav-'nly com-fort fraught!
Some-times where E - den's bow-ers bloom,
Nor ev - er mur - mur nor re - pine;
When by Thy grace the vic-t'ry's won,

What - e'er I do, wher - e'er I be,
By wa - ters calm, o'er trou - bled sea,
Con - tent, what - ev - er lot I see,
E'en death's cold wave I will not flee,

Still 'tis God's hand that lead-eth me.
Still 'tis His hand that lead-eth me.
Since 'tis my God that lead-eth me.
Since God thro' Jor - dan lead-eth me.

REFRAIN

He lead-eth me, He lead-eth me:

By His own hand He lead-eth me:

His faith-ful fol-low'r I would be,

For by His hand He lead-eth me.

343

ALL THE WAY MY SAVIOUR LEADS ME

FANNY J. CROSBY

ROBERT LOWRY

8s, 7s.

FANNY CROSBY, the blind hymn-writer, was in desperate financial difficulty. She could think of no way in which to get some money, so she asked the Lord for help. The next day, a man called at her home and handed her the money she needed. In telling the story herself, she said: "I have no way to account for this, except to believe that God, in answer to my prayer, put it into the heart of this good man to bring me the money."

1. All the way my Sav-iour leads me; What have I to ask be-side? Can I doubt His ten-der mer-cy, Who through life has been my Guide?

2. All the way my Sav-iour leads me; Cheers each wind-ing path I tread, Gives me grace for ev'ry tri-al, Feeds me with the liv-ing bread.

3. All the way my Sav-iour leads me; Oh, the full-ness of His love! Per-fect rest to me is prom-ised In my Fa-ther's house a-bove.

Heav'n - ly peace, di - vin - est
Though my wea - ry steps may
When my spir - it, clothed im -

com-fort, Here by faith in Him to dwell!
fal-ter, And my soul a-thirst may be,
mor-tal, Wings its flight to realms of day,

For I know, what-e'er be - fall me, Je-sus
Gush-ing from the Rock be - fore me, Lo! a
This my song thro' end-less a - ges: Je-sus

1.
do - eth all things well;
spring of joy I see;
led me all the way;

2.
well.
see.
way.

LEANING ON THE EVERLASTING ARMS

ELISHA A. HOFFMAN   ANTHONY J. SHOWALTER

Leaning on Jesus,
10.9.10.9., with refrain

THE REVEREND Mr. Hoffman was a Congregational minister. He spent many years at Lebanon, Pa., where he wrote numerous hymns. In writing this hymn, he had been furnished with words and music of the refrain which were written by Showalter, a singing-school teacher of Hartsells, Ala. The sentiment is founded on DEUTERONOMY 33:27, "Underneath are the everlasting arms."

1. What a fel-low-ship, what a joy di-vine,
2. Oh, how sweet to walk in this pil-grim way,
3. What have I to dread, what have I to fear,

Lean - ing on the ev - er - last - ing arms;
Lean - ing on the ev - er - last - ing arms;
Lean - ing on the ev - er - last - ing arms;

What a bless-ed-ness, what a peace is mine,
Oh, how bright the path grows from day to day,
I have bless-ed peace with my Lord so near,

Lean-ing on the ev-er-last-ing arms.
Lean-ing on the ev-er-last-ing arms.
Lean-ing on the ev-er-last-ing arms.

CHORUS

Lean - ing, lean - ing,
Lean-ing on Je-sus, lean-ing on Je-sus,

Safe and se-cure from all a-larms; Lean - ing,
Leaning on Je-sus,

lean - ing, Lean-ing on the ev-er-last-ing arms.
lean-ing on Je-sus,

347

GOD BE WITH YOU TILL WE MEET AGAIN

JEREMIAH E. RANKIN   9.8.8.9   WILLIAM G. TOMER

DR. RANKIN, A CONGREGATIONAL MINISTER who in 1889 became president of Howard University in Washington, D.C., used this hymn to close his evening services. In his own account of the writing he tells how impressed he was to learn from his dictionary that "goodbye" is a contraction of "God be with ye." The hymn was sung extensively at the revival meetings of Moody, Sankey and others, and was adopted by Christian Endeavor. Purists have found the refrain objectionable, but no one claims literary value for the hymn, only an appeal so great it cannot be questioned.

1. God be with you till we meet a - gain;
2. God be with you till we meet a - gain;
3. God be with you till we meet a - gain;
4. God be with you till we meet a - gain;

By His coun - sels guide, up - hold you,
'Neath His wings pro - tect - ing hide you,
When life's per - ils thick con - found you,
Keep love's ban - ner float - ing o'er you;

With His sheep se - cure - ly fold you;
Dai - ly man - na still pro - vide you;
Put His arms un - fail - ing 'round you;
Smite death's threat - 'ning wave be - fore you;

348

God be with you till we meet a - gain.
God be with you till we meet a - gain.
God be with you till we meet a - gain.
God be with you till we meet a - gain.

CHORUS

Till we meet, _____ till we meet, _____ Till we
Till we meet, till we meet,

meet at Je - sus' _ feet; Till we
till we meet;

meet, _____ till we meet, _ God be
Till we meet, till we meet,

with you till we meet a - gain.

THE LORD BLESS YOU AND KEEP YOU

Numbers 6:24-26

PETER CHRISTIAN LUTKIN

NO BENEDICTION the Holy Bible contains is more beautifully poetic than this one and no musical setting for it has been so favored as Dr. Lutkin's; ASCAP still lists seventeen special arrangements being sold by different music publishers. Dr. Lutkin was a founder of the American Guild of Organists in 1896 and an editor of early hymnals for both the Methodist and Protestant Episcopal Churches. He studied, performed and composed in many American and European lands. The King James text for this benediction is "The Lord bless *thee* and keep *thee*," using the singular.

The Lord bless you and keep you, The Lord lift His coun-te-nance up-on you; And give you peace, and give you peace, The Lord make His face to shine up-on you, And be gra-cious un-to you, be gra-cious un-to you. A-men.

RECESSIONAL

Arr. Elise Bretton   FOLKINGHAM (1708)   Rudyard Kipling

Victoria became queen in 1837 and had a golden jubilee in 1887. In 1897, knowing she could not last 75 years, Parliament changed the rules and made a diamond jubilee of the 60th year. Nearly all European royalty and war-lords attended ("the captains and the kings"), and at the end Kipling—no favorite of his queen—struck a somber note in commentary, one that might have occurred to Americans as the sun set on V-J Day. Charles Wood and other contemporary composers set Recessional to music, but most hymnals have preferred the Folkingham tune that it fits so well.

1. God of our fa - thers, known of old, Lord of our far-flung bat - tle line, be - neath Whose aw - ful hand we hold do - min - ion o - ver palm and pine, Lord God of hosts be with us yet, Lest we for-get, Lest we for - get.

2. The tu - mult and the shout-ing dies, The cap - tains and the kings de - part. Still stands Thine an - cient sac - ri - fice, An hum - ble and a con - trite heart. Lord God of hosts be with us yet, Lest we for-get, Lest we for - get.

3. Far called, our na - vies melt a - way; On dune and head-land sinks the fire. Lo, all our pomp of yes - ter-day is one with Nin - e - veh and Tyre. Judge of the na - tions, spare us yet, Lest we for-get, Lest we for - get.

4. If drunk with sight of pow'r we loose wild tongues that have not Thee in awe, Such boast-ings as the Gen - tiles use or less - er breeds with - out the law Lord God of hosts be with us yet, Lest we for-get, Lest we for - get.

5. For hea - then heart that puts her trust In reek - ing tube and i - ron shard, All val - iant dust that builds on dust, And, guard-ing, calls not Thee to guard, For fran - tic boast and fool - ish word Thy mer - cy on Thy peo - ple Lord.

I KNOW THAT MY REDEEMER LIVES

CHARLES WESLEY F.M. **GEORGE F. HANDEL**

FROM THE MESSIAH, Handel's (and the world's) most celebrated oratorio, the prolific Dr. Wesley abstracted and popularized this as a hymn. The Biblical source is Job 19:25, "For I know that my redeemer liveth, and that he shall stand at the latter day upon the earth"; the words were spoken by Job. This is a favored recessional hymn in some churches.

1. I know that my Re-
2. He lives, tri - um - phant
3. He lives, that I may
4. Let strains of heav'n - ly

deem - er lives, And ev - er prays for
o'er the grave, At God's right hand on
al - so live, And now His grace pro -
mu - sic rise, While all their an - them

me; A to - ken of His love He
high, My ran - somed soul to keep and
claim; He lives, that I may hon - or
sing to Christ, my pre - cious sac - ri -

gives, A pledge of lib - er - ty.
save To bless and glo - ri - fy.
give, To His most ho - ly name.
fice, And ev - er - liv - ing King.

CHRISTMAS CAROLS

O COME, ALL YE FAITHFUL

Translated by
FREDERIC OAKELEY

JOHN FRANCIS WADE'S
Cantus Diversi

Adeste Fideles, P.M., irregular

THIS HYMN, in its Latin form (Adeste Fideles), has been popular since 1700 at least, and was sung in France before reaching England. It may still be considered anonymous, but an early manuscript recently found may point to Wade, a copyist of the early 18th century, as the author. Canon Oakeley's translation is his second version. The first was published in 1852. There is as much disagreement about the words as about the tune.

1. Oh, come all ye faith-ful, Joy-ful and tri-umph-ant, Oh, come ye, Oh, come ye to Beth-le-hem. Come and be-

2. Sing, cho-rus of An-gels, Sing in ex-ul-ta-tion, Oh, sing all ye cit-i-zens of heav'n a-bove; Glo-ry to

hold Him, Born the King of An - gels:
God___ In the high-est, glo - ry!

REFRAIN

Oh, come, let us a - dore Him, Oh,

come let us a - dore Him, Oh, come, let us a -

dore Him,___ Christ___ the Lord.

SILENT NIGHT! HOLY NIGHT!

Freely translated from
JOSEPH MOHR
FRANZ GRUBER

Stille Nacht, 6.6.8.8.6.6.

SOME GREAT MASTERPIECES have been the result of patience and long years of work. Others, equally great, seem to spring into existence in a few moments. So it was that on December 24, 1818, with just a few hours before the Christmas service, and the organ out of commission, Father Mohr and the organist Franz Grüber wrote a hymn for two voices and sang it themselves, with Grüber furnishing a guitar accompaniment. No fewer than eleven dramas, in German and English, have been based upon real and imaginary stories of the hymn.

1. Si - lent night! ho - ly night!
2. Si - lent night! ho - ly night!
8. Si - lent night! ho - ly night!

All is calm, all is bright;
Dark - ness flies, all is light;
Won - drous Star, lend thy light!

'Round yon vir - gin moth - er and Child,
Shep - herds hear the an - gels sing:
With the an - gels let us sing

Ho - ly In - fant so ten - der and mild;
Al - le - lu - ia! hail__ the King!
Al - le - lu - ia to____ our King!

Sleep in heav - en - ly peace,__
Christ the Sav - iour is born,__
Christ the Sav - iour is born,__

Sleep__ in heav - en - ly peace.__
Christ__ the Sav - iour is born.__
Christ__ the Sav - iour is born.__

AWAY IN A MANGER

ANONYMOUS

JAMES R. MURRAY

Mueller, four 11s

THIS HYMN has always been known as *Luther's Cradle Hymn.* Hymnologists, however, and especially biographers of Luther, were disturbed by the fact that it is not to be found in any of his works, nor does it conform to his style. Penetrating research by Richard S. Hill disclosed the true story, published in his article, "Not So Far Away in a Manger: Forty-one Settings of an American Carol," in the December, 1945, issue of *The Music Library Association Notes.* The facts are: The words are anonymous, probably written about 1880, and there is no doubt that the tune was written by James R. Murray, in 1887, and first appeared in a book of songs for children copyrighted by the John Church Company of Cincinnati, in 1887.

1. A - way in a man - ger, No
2. The cat - tle are low - ing, The

crib for a bed, The lit - tle Lord
poor ba - by wakes, But lit - tle Lord

Je - sus laid down His sweet
Je - sus, No cry - ing He

head; The stars in the sky Looked
makes; I love Thee, Lord Je - sus! Look

down where He lay, The lit - tle Lord
down from the sky And stay by my

Je - sus, A - sleep on the hay.
cra - dle To watch lull - a - by.

HARK, THE HERALD ANGELS SING

CHARLES WESLEY   FELIX MENDELSSOHN

Mendelssohn
7.7.7.7.D., with refrain

THIS IS ONE of the most important Christmas hymns, written in 1738 and sung every year since. It is considered Wesley's best writing, second only to *Jesus, Lover of My Soul*. The tune was written in 1840 (as part of Mendelssohn's *Festgesang* in celebration of the invention of printing), and was adapted for the hymn by William H. Cummings, in 1856. Mendelssohn himself considered the tune unsuitable for sacred words.

1. Hark! the her - ald an-gels sing,—
2. Christ, by high - est heav'n a - dored;—
3. Hail the heav'n - born Prince of Peace!—

"Glo - ry to the new-born King; Peace on earth, and
Christ, the ev - er - last-ing Lord; Late in time be-
Hail the Sun of Righteous-ness! Ris'n with heal-ing

mer - cy mild,— God and sin - ners rec - on - ciled!"
hold him come,— Off-spring of the Vir-gin's womb:
in his wings: Light and life to all he brings;

Joy-ful, all ye na-tions rise,_ Join the tri-umphs
Veiled in flesh the God-head see;_ Hail th'in-car-nate
Mild he lays his glo-ry by,_ Born that man no

of the skies;With th'an-gel-ic host pro-claim,
De - i - ty!_Pleased as man with men to dwell;
more may die:_ Born to raise the sons of earth,

Christ is_born in Beth-le-hem!
Je - sus, our Im-man-u - el! } Hark!the her-ald
Born to_give them sec-ond birth.

an-gels sing,"Glo - ry_ to the new-born King!"

361

IT CAME UPON A MIDNIGHT CLEAR

EDMUND H. SEARS

RICHARD STORRS WILLIS

Carol, C.M.D.

THIS IS an American hymn, written in Boston in 1849. It is based on the Unitarian convictions of the writers, a radical position in that day. Perhaps because of this factor, it was not published in many hymnals for a long time, until public demand prevailed. We include, as being applicable to modern times, the original third stanza (the second stanza given here). The tune *Carol* is from Willis' *Study No. 23.*

1. It came up-on— the mid-night clear, That
2. Be-neath the an - gels' strain have rolled Two
3. For lo, the days are has-t'ning on, By

glo - rious song— of old,— From
thou - sand years— of wrong;— Yet
proph - et bards— fore - told,— When

an-gels bend - ing near the earth To
with the woes of sin and strife The
with the ev - er - cir-cling years Comes

touch their harps_ of gold:_ "Peace
world has suf - fered long:_ And
round the age_ of gold;_ When

on the earth,_ good will to men, From
man, at war_ with man, hears not The
peace shall o - ver all the earth Its

heav'n's all - gra-cious King:" The world in sol-emn
love song which they bring; Oh, hush the noise, ye
an - cient splen-dors fling, And the whole world give

still-ness lay To hear the an - gels sing.
men of strife, And hear the an - gels sing!
back the song Which now the an - gels sing.

JOY TO THE WORLD

Isaac Watts

Lowell Mason
from themes by Handel

Antioch, C.M.

Sir Isaac Watts gave a joyful interpretation to the beautiful 98th Psalm. It is a Christmas hymn, celebrating the Nativity, and calling upon all nature to join in solemn exultation. Lowell Mason, in 1830, provided the setting by making a composite of two Handelian themes, *Lift Up Your Heads* and *Comfort Ye*, both from the *Messiah*.

1. Joy to the world! the Lord is come; Let earth re-ceive her King;— Let ev-'ry heart pre-
2. Joy to the world! the Sav-iour reigns; Let men their songs em-ploy;— While fields_ and_ floods,_ rocks,
3. He rules the world with truth and grace, And makes the na-tions prove_ The glo-ries_ of_ His

pare__ Him__ room,_____ and
hills__ and__ plains,_____ Re -
right - eous - ness,_____ And

heav'n and na - ture__ sing, And__
peat the sound - ing__ joy, Re -
won - ders of His__ love, And__

heav'n and na - ture__ sing, And__
peat the sound - ing__ joy, Re -
won - ders of His__ love, And__

heav'n, And heav'n__ and na - ture sing.
peat, Re - peat___ the sound-ing joy.
won-ders, And won - ders of His love.

O LITTLE TOWN OF BETHLEHEM

PHILLIPS BROOKS   **LEWIS H. REDNER**

St. Louis, irregular

BISHOP BROOKS of Massachusetts made a pilgrimage to Jerusalem and the Holy Land in 1867, when he was still a young man. Late one night, from a hilltop, he looked down upon the sleeping village of Bethlehem, and received inspiration for his greatest hymn. He gave the poem to his organist and Sunday school superintendent, Lewis H. Redner, who waited until the following Christmas Eve before composing the tune. Only after 25 years had passed was this carol generally included in hymnals.

1. O lit-tle town of Beth-le-hem, How
2. How si-lent-ly, how si-lent-ly The
3. O ho-ly Child of Beth-le-hem, De-

still we_ see thee lie! A - bove thy deep and
won-drous gift is giv'n! So God im-parts to
scend to_ us we pray; Cast out our sin and

dream-less sleep The si - lent_ stars go
hu - man hearts The bless-ings_ of His
en - ter in, Be born in_ us to -

by; Yet in thy dark streets shin-eth The
heav'n. No ear may hear His com-ing; But
day. We hear the Christ-mas an-gels The

ev-er-last-ing Light; The hopes and fears of
in this world of sin, Where meek souls will re-
great glad ti-dings tell, O come to us, a-

all the years Are met in thee to-night.
ceive Him still, The dear Christ en-ters in.
bide with us, Our Lord Em-man-u-el!

WHAT CHILD IS THIS?

WILLIAM C. DIX   Greensleeves   *Arr.* JOHN STAINER

DIX, A BUSINESSMAN who for a hobby was a moderately prolific writer of hymns, wrote the words in 1878 for a carol he called *The Manger Throne*, which was fairly successful set to another tune. The great present popularity of the carol was achieved when the verses were found to fit ideally a time-honored English melody popular during the times of Queen Elizabeth (I) and twice alluded to by Shakespeare. The original words to this melody, *My Lady Greensleeves*, are hardly understandable now. The C in the melody (measures 1, 5, 9, 13) is often sung as C-sharp.

1. What Child is this, who laid to rest, On Mary's lap is sleep - ing? Whom an - gels greet with
2. Why lies He in such mean es - tate, Where ox and ass are feed - ing? Good Christ - ian fear, for
3. So bring Him in - cense, gold, and myrrh, Come peas - ant king, to own Him. The King of kings sal -

an - thems sweet, While shep - herds watch are keep - ing?
sin - ners here, The si - lent word is plead - ing?
va - tion brings, Let lov - ing hearts en - throne Him.

REFRAIN

This, this is Christ the King, Whom
Nails, spear, shall pierce Him through, The
Raise, raise the song on high, The

shep - herds guard and an - gels sing; Haste, haste to
Cross be borne for me, for you: Hail, hail the
Vir - gin sing her lul - la - by: Joy, joy for

bring Him laud,
Word made flesh, } The Babe, the Son of Ma - ry.
Christ is born,

DECK THE HALLS

Traditional Welsh

THE POPULARITY OF THIS CAROL, and its applicability to Christmas, are relatively recent. It is a "secular" song, having seasonal rather than religious implications; strictly, it applies less to Christmas than to New Year's festivities. The burning of the Yule (log), the boar's head, and decorations of holly and mistletoe derive from winter celebrations that antedate by hundreds of years the advent of Christianity in Great Britain, and the nonsense tra-la-la refrain is medieval.

1. Deck the halls with boughs of hol - ly,
2. See the blaz - ing yule be - fore us,
3. Fast a - way the old year pass - es,

Fa la la la la, la la la la,

'Tis the sea - son to be jol - ly,
Strike the harp and join the cho - rus,
Hail the new, ye lads and lass - es,

Fa la la la la, la la la la; Don we now our
Fol - low me in
Sing we joy - ous

gay ap - par - el,
mer - ry meas - ure,
all to - geth - er,
Fa la la, la la la

la la la!
Troll the an - cient Christ-mas car - ol,
While I tell of Christ-mas treas - ure,
Heed - less of the wind and weath - er,

Fa la la la la, la la la la!

GOD REST YOU MERRY, GENTLEMEN

ANONYMOUS   *Arranged by* JOHN STAINER

OBSERVE the placement of the comma, making the first line and title mean "God make you happy, gentlemen." In style and form, this carol seems to be a product of early England, but actually it dates from the sixteenth century. Characteristic of an earlier period, however, is the coupling of a minor melody with joyful words. Sir John Stainer (1840-1901) wrote many cantatas, anthems, and songs, in addition to textbooks on music. His *Treatise on Harmony* was a standard work for thirty years.

1. God rest you mer - ry, gen - tle - men, Let
2. From God our heaven - ly Fa - ther A
3. "Fear not, then," said the an - gel, "Let
4. Now to the Lord sing prais - es, All

noth - ing you dis - may, Re - mem - ber Christ our
bless - ed an - gel came; And un - to cer - tain
noth - ing you af - fright, This day is born a
you with - in this place, And with true love an

Sav - iour Was born on Christ - mas Day; To
shep - herds Brought ti - dings of the same; How
Sav - iour Of a pure Vir - gin bright, To
broth - er - hood Each oth - er now em - brace; This

save us all from Sa - tan's power When
that in Beth - le - hem was born The
free all those who trust in Him From
ho - ly tide of Christ - mas All

we were gone a stray
Son of God by name."
oth - ers doth de - face

REFRAIN

O___ ti - dings of
com - fort and joy, Com-fort and joy; O___
ti - dings of com - fort and joy.

373

THE FIRST NOWELL

ANONYMOUS

THE FIRST printed copy on record is dated 1823, but the carol was known for some time before. A collection edited by William Sandys, *Christmas Carols, Ancient and Modern* (1833), contained a revised version. Nowell is from the French *Nöel*, or Christmas, and *Noel* is, in turn, from the Latin *natalis*, birthday. Certain features of this carol suggest that it may be a "translation" from very ancient material of Olde Englande.

1. The first Now-ell the an-gel did
2. They look-ed up and saw a
3. This star drew nigh to the north-
4. Then en-ter'd in there Wise-men

say Was to cer-tain poor shep-herds in
star Shin-ing in the East be-
west, O'er Beth-le-hem it
three, Full rev-'rent-ly up-

fields as they lay. In fields where they lay
yond them far, And to the earth it
took its rest, And there it did both
on their knee, And of-fer'd there in

keep-ing their sheep On a cold win-ter's
gave_ great light, And_ so it con-
stop_ and stay Right_ o - ver the
His_ pres - ence, Their_ gold_ and

night_ that was_ so deep.
tin - ued both day_ and night.
place_ where Je - sus lay.
myrrh_ and frank - in - cense.

REFRAIN

Now - ell,_ Now - ell, Now - ell, Now ell,_

Born is the King_ of Is - ra - el.

375

WE THREE KINGS OF ORIENT ARE

Kings of Orient   JOHN HENRY HOPKINS

DR. HOPKINS, AN ANGLICAN RECTOR, wrote both words and music in 1857. They vie with each other in excellence and the music is so imaginative that according to Wallace Brockway (in *A Treasury of Hymns*, 1953) many critics could not credit Dr. Hopkins with the composition and assumed him to be merely the arranger. Strictly the carol applies to Epiphany, January 6, when the gifts of the Magi (Matthew 2:11) were presented. In legend the Magi were named Kaspar, Melchior, and Balthazar; and one was a Negro, emphasizing the absence of racial discrimination in the Christian ethic.

1. We three kings of O - ri - ent are,
2. Born a babe on Beth - le - hem's plain,
3. Frank - in - cense to of - fer have I;
4. Myrrh is mine; its bit - ter per - fume
5. Glo - rious now be - hold__ Him rise,

Bear - ing gifts we trav - erse far
Gold we bring to crown Him a - gain;
In - cense owns a De - i - ty nigh,
Breathes a life of gath - 'ring gloom;
King and God and Sac - ri - fice;

Field and foun - tain, moor and moun - tain,
King for - ev - er, ceas - ing nev - er,
Pray'r and prais - ing all men rais - ing,
Sorr'w - ing, sigh - ing, bleed - ing, dy - ing,
Heav'n sings "Hal - le - lu - jah!" "Hal - le -

Fol - low - ing yon - der Star.
O - ver us all to reign.
Wor - ship God on high.
Sealed in the stone - cold tomb.
lu - jah!" earth re - plies.

REFRAIN
Oh,— star of won-der, star of might, Star with

roy - al beau-ty bright, West - ward lead-ing,

still pro - ceed-ing, Guide us to the per - fect light.

377

THE TWELVE DAYS OF CHRISTMAS

Traditional

THIS CAROL is of old English or Scottish origin. Since the advent of radio and television, it has become well known throughout the United States; before that it was known chiefly in the eastern states, usually in versions adapted to more familiar symbolic materials than, for example, "ten lords a-leaping." The twelve days are those between Christmas and Epiphany (December 25 to January 6). In some Appalachian regions the Julian calendar obtains, with "Old Christmas" on January 6 and "New Christmas" on December 25. This song is of the type called accumulative.

On the first day of Christ - mas My true love sent to me, A par - tridge in a pear tree. On the

2. sec - ond day of Christ - mas My true love sent to me,

Two tur - tle doves, and a par - tridge in a pear

tree. On the third day of Christ-mas My true love sent to me,

Three French hens, two tur - tle doves, and a

par - tridge in a pear tree. On the

fourth day of Christ - mas My true love sent to me,

Four call - ing birds, three French hens,

two tur-tle doves, and a par-tridge in a pear

tree. On the fifth day of Christ-mas My

true love sent to me, Five gold rings,

four call-ing birds, three French hens,

two tur-tle doves, and a par-tridge in a pear tree. On the

GOOD KING WENCESLAS

John Mason Neale

from Piae Cantiones

Wenceslaus (as his name is latinized) was reigning Duke of Bohemia, died about 936 A.D., was canonized in the 11th century and is patron saint of Bohemia. This popular carol, for which Dr. Neale wrote the verses in 1853, commemorates one of the deeds of kindness for which Wenceslas was noted—and sainted. The tune, in this version taken from an old Swedish Lutheran hymnal, is used also for the "springtime carol" *Tempus adest floridum* (the time, or season, of flowers is here). The feast day of St. Stephen, the first Christian martyr (Acts 7:59), is December 26.

1. Good King Wen-ces-las looked out, On the feast of Ste-phen,
2. "Hith-er page, and stand by me, If thou knows't it tell-ing,
3. "Bring me flesh and bring me wine, Bring me pine logs hith-er:
4. "Sire, the night is dark-er now, And the wind grows strong-er;
5. In his mas-ter's steps he trod, Where the snow lay dint-ed;

When the snow lay round a-bout, Deep and crisp and e-ven.
Yon-der peas-ant, who is he? Where and what his dwell-ing?"
Thou and I shall see him dine, When we bear them thith-er."
Fails my heart, I know not how; I can go no long-er."
Heat was in the ver-y sod Which the Saint had print-ed.

Bright-ly shone the moon that night, Though the frost was cru-el,
"Sire, he lives a good league hence, Un-der-neath the moun-tain,
Page and mon-arch, forth they went, Forth they went to-geth-er;
"Mark my foot-steps, my good page, Tread thou in them bold-ly;
There-fore, Christ-ian men be sure, Wealth or rank pos-sess-ing,

When a poor man came in sight, Gath-'ring win-ter fu-el.
Right a-gainst the for-est fence, By Saint Ag-nes' foun-tain."
Through the rude winds wild la-ment, And the bit-ter weath-er.
Thou shalt find the win-ter's rage Freeze thy blood less cold-ly."
Ye who now will bless the poor, Shall your-selves find bless-ing.

SPIRITUALS

STEAL AWAY TO JESUS

Negro Spiritual

In 1872 the famous Jubilee Singers, of the then new Fisk University, visited England. They sang for Queen Victoria, and their first rendition, at the request of the Duke of Argyll, was STEAL AWAY TO JESUS. So impressed was the Queen that she extended the full hospitality of London to the party of American singers. As with many other spirituals, this beautiful and tender melody is based on the pentatonic, or five-tone scale.

Steal a-way, steal a-way,

steal a-way to Je-sus! Steal a-way,

steal a-way home, I ain't got long to stay here.

Fine

1. My Lord___ calls me, He calls me by the
2. Green trees are_ bend-ing, Poor sin-ner stand a-
8. My Lord___ calls me, He calls me by the

thun - der;
trem - bling; } The trump - et sounds it
light - ning;

in - a my soul: I ain't got long to stay here.

D. C.

SWING LOW, SWEET CHARIOT

Negro Spiritual

LIKE OTHER FORMS of folk expression, the spirituals of the Negro have a deep basis of originality. Scales and modes are often found that do not conform to the types in general use. SWING LOW, SWEET CHARIOT is founded on a pentatonic, or five-tone, scale, often used in songs of the American Indians. Anton Dvorâk used the melody in his symphony *From the New World*. The Fisk Jubilee Singers visited London in 1875, during the tour of Dwight Moody and Ira Sankey. Their rendition of this soft, poignant spiritual brought tears to the eyes of the great revivalists, and Moody asked the singers to take part in the service at the Haymarket Opera House, where they received an enthusiastic welcome.

SOLO

Swing low, sweet char-i-ot,—

CHORUS

Com-ing for to car-ry me home, Swing low, sweet

Fine

char-i-ot,— Com-ing for to car-ry me home.

1. I looked o - ver Jor - dan and
2. If you get there be -
3. I'm some - times up and

what did I see,
fore I do, } Com-ing for to car-ry me
some-times down,

home, { A band of an - gels
Just tell my friends I'm
But still my soul feels

D. C. al Fine

com-ing af-ter me,
com - ing too, } Com-ing for to car-ry me home.
heav'n-ly bound,

387

DEEP RIVER

Negro Spiritual

SAMUEL COLERIDGE TAYLOR was an English composer of African Negro descent. In 1905 he published *Twenty-Four Negro Melodies, Transcribed for the Piano,* and from this source the celebrated American violinist Maud Powell made her concert arrangement of DEEP RIVER. She featured it while on tour with her own concert group, before and during World War I. This departure, and a later transcription by Henry Thacker Burleigh, may have been responsible for the entrance of spirituals into the repertory of serious concert programming.

Deep____ Riv-er, My home is o-ver Jor-dan,____ Deep____ Riv-er, Lord, I want to cross o-ver in-to camp-ground.

(hum)

1. Oh, don't you want to go to that Gos-pel feast, That
2. I'm go-ing in to Heav-en and take my seat,
3. Oh, when I get to Heav-en I'll walk all about, There's

(hum)

prom-is'd land — Where all is peace?}
Cast my crown — At Je-sus' feet. } Lord, I
no - one there — To turn me out.

D. C. al Fine

want to cross o - ver in - to camp - ground.

LORD, I'M TROUBLIN'

THIS BEAUTIFUL SPIRITUAL is well known to thousands of persons, especially among Negroes; but for some reason it has not previously appeared in print, so far as the editors can determine. The editors have heard it sung in many parts of the southern United States, in Connecticut, and in Wisconsin. W. C. Handy, in his eightieth year, told the editors that he remembered it from the age of five. The version here presented was sung by a group of field hands on a South Carolina plantation. It is harmonized, so far as it is possible to remember, exactly as they sang it, the intention being to avoid all "copy-book" formalization.

ALL GOD'S CHILDREN GOT SHOES

Negro Spiritual

THIS TRADITIONAL SONG, which was in the repertory of the Fisk Jubilee Singers, has no determinable title. It may be called, after one of its verses, "I've got a robe," or "I've got shoes." Surely it is now widely known by the title, *All God's Chillun Got Wings*, which Eugene O'Neill adopted for one of his most successful plays (on the subject of miscegenation). The editors selected as the title the designation they have most often heard.

1. I got-a shoes, You got-a shoes; All God's chil-dren got-a shoes; ___ When I get to Heav-en goin' to put on my shoes, goin' to walk all o-ver God's Heav-en, ___ Heav-en, ___ Heav-en, ___ Ev'-ry-bod-y talk-in' 'bout Heaven ain't go-in' there, Heav-en.

2. I got-a robe, You got-a robe; All God's chil-dren got-a robe; ___ When I get to Heav-en goin' to put on my robe, goin' to shout all o-ver God's Heav-en, ___ Heav-en, ___ Heav-en, ___ Ev'-ry-bod-y talk-in' 'bout Heaven ain't go-in' there, Heav-en.

3. I got-a wings, You got-a wings; All God's chil-dren got-a wings; ___ When I get to Heav-en goin' to put on my wings, goin' to fly all o-ver God's Heav-en, ___ Heav-en, ___ Heav-en, ___ Ev'-ry-bod-y talk-in' 'bout Heaven ain't go-in' there, Heav-en.

4. I got-a harp, You got-a harp; All God's chil-dren got-a harp; ___ When I get to Heav-en goin' to take out my harp, goin' to sing all o-ver God's Heav-en, ___ Heav-en, ___ Heav-en, ___ Ev'-ry-bod-y talk-in' 'bout Heaven ain't go-in' there, Heav-en.

I AM A POOR WAYFARING STRANGER

White Spiritual

DURING the great revivals and camp meetings that spread from the Kentucky frontier after the Revolutionary War, many white spirituals appeared. They seem to have been influenced by Elizabethan modes and are usually best for solo voice, thereby differing from the Negro musical forms with their more exotic scales and ready harmonizations. The great folk-singer Burl Ives is responsible for the popularization (in the late 1940s) of this spiritual, and is professionally "billed" as "the Wayfaring Stranger."

I am a poor__ way-far-ing stran-ger,__ A - trav-'ling through this world of woe;__ Yet there's no sick - ness, toil or danger__ In that bright world to which I go.__ I'm go-ing home to see my moth-er,__ I'm go-ing there no more to roam, I'm just a go-ing o-ver Jor-dan,__ I'm just a - go-ing o-ver home.

NOBODY KNOWS THE TROUBLE I'VE SEEN

Negro Spiritual

THIS IS the stirring cry of a people in bondage, and one of the most familiar true spirituals. The Jubilee Singers of Fisk University originally used a minor tune, and a rather different text, which also appears in the W. C. Handy collection. However, the editors of this collection have preferred to use the popular version. An arrangement of this spiritual by Henry Thacker Burleigh, for many years organist at New York's Grace Church, was introduced in 1917.

No-bod-y knows the trou-ble I've seen, No-bod-y knows, but Je - sus, No-bod - y knows the trou-ble I've seen,

Fine

Glor - y, hal - le - lu - jah! Some - times I'm up, some-times I'm down, yes, my Lord!__ Some - times I'm al-most

D.C. al Fine

down to the ground, Yes,__ my__ Lord!__

I'M GOING DOWN TO THE RIVER OF JORDAN

Traditional

THIS MAY WELL BE one of the spirituals out of the American South that nobody wrote, that "just grew." It may be of white or Negro origin, but the editors have heard it sung most often by Negroes. Anyone who has attended a camp meeting, mass baptism, or revival will comprehend the process: the preacher's impassioned invocation; from here and there a fervent "Amen!" or "Yes, Lord!"; a phrase improvised by a strong singer, a response from the congregation, another phrase, another response, and gradual attainment of musical shape and form. This, one of the oldest and best-loved spirituals, for some reason has seldom appeared in print.

Jor - dan some of these days Hal - le - lu - jah!
Slip - pers some of these days Hal - le - lu - jah!
Choir___ some of these days Hal - le - lu - jah!
Je - sus some of these days Hal - le - lu - jah!

I'm___ go - ing down to the Riv - er of
I'm___ going to put on those Sil - ver
I'm___ going to sing in the Heav - en - ly
I'm___ going to sit down a - by___ my

Jor - dan, I'm go - ing down to the
Slip - pers, I'm going to put on those
Choir___ I'm going to sing in the
Je - sus, I'm going to sit down a -

Riv - er of Jor - dan some of these days.___
Sil - ver Slip - pers some of these days.___
Heav - en - ly Choir___ some of these days.___
by___ my Je - sus some of these days.___

396

INDEX

Titles of songs are in **boldface type;** *first lines* of songs are in *italic type;* NAMES of composers, authors, translators, arrangers and other persons are in SMALL CAPITALS. In this Index all entries are arranged strictly alphabetically. See also the Table of Contents, page vii, for a listing of songs in order of appearance and by classification.

INDEX

398

INDEX

INDEX

INDEX

INDEX

INDEX

INDEX

AMENS